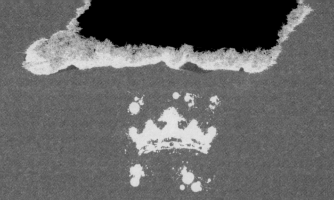

The SCHOLASTIC CLASSICS were chosen very carefully -- these are our favourite books, and we want them to become your favourites too. There's a reason they've been around for so long. They're just great stories, no matter how old you are or how long it's been since they were written. They may mean something different to everyone who reads them, but they always mean something.

The books you read when you're young live on in your mind for ever. We think these ones are worth the space.

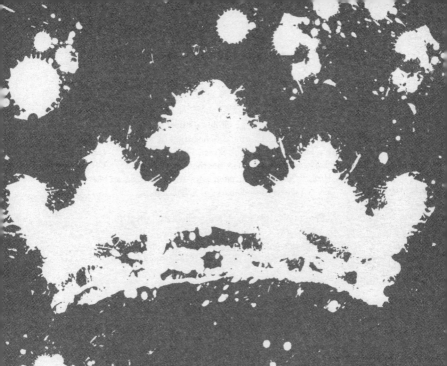

MACBETH

William Shakespeare

■SCHOLASTIC

Scholastic Children's Books
An imprint of Scholastic Ltd
Euston House, 24 Eversholt Street, London, NW1 1DB, UK
Registered office: Westfield Road, Southam, Warwickshire, CV47 0RA
SCHOLASTIC and associated logos are trademarks and/or
registered trademarks of Scholastic Inc.

First published in the UK by Scholastic Ltd, 2019

ISBN 978 1407 19326 7

A CIP catalogue record for this book
is available from the British Library.

Printed by CPI Group (UK) Ltd, Croydon, CR0 4YY
Papers used by Scholastic Children's Books are made
from wood grown in sustainable forests.

1 3 5 7 9 10 8 6 4 2

www.scholastic.co.uk

CONTENTS

FOREWORD

When studying *Macbeth*, it is necessary to understand the social, historical and political context, as well as the world of the play in terms of its setting, the characters and their emotions, motivations and relationships with other characters. One of the most important aspects of the text is Shakespeare's use of language and the different way in which characters speak, imagery is created, and language is used to convey a sense of time, place and to create atmosphere.

A play for performance

To fully understand Shakespeare's plays it is necessary to realize that they were written to be performed not to be read. Shakespeare himself was an actor as well as playwright. Women were not allowed to perform upon the stage and all the female roles would have been played by teenage boys whose voices had not yet broken. The actors would have given the bare bones of a script, but the play that was shown to the paying audience was developed through the actors exploring the characters' emotions, motivations and relationships on stage. The plays had very simple sets, no sound or lighting and would be performed during the day. Therefore, there are references to the time of day, the weather and the location, as well as major events that have taken place being reported.

Theatre in Shakespeare's time was a popular form of entertainment for all social classes from the "groundlings" who paid a small amount to stand and watch the performance, to the upper classes who sat on the balcony dressed in all their finery, as much part of the spectacle as the plays themselves. The plays of William Shakespeare were extremely popular and *Macbeth*, a tragedy about a man brought down by his one failing (his and his scheming wife's ambition that he should be King), was no exception.

HISTORICAL CONTEXT

The story behind the play and why it was chosen

Many of Shakespeare's plays were sourced from well-known stories from the past rather than being original works. The themes and issues explored in his plays are just as relevant today as they were in Shakespeare's time and at the time the stories the plays are based on were written. *Macbeth*, like many of Shakespeare's plays, was based on historical fact but with changes made to flatter the King. In the original historical account Banquo assists Macbeth in the killing of the King, but as King James I was believed at the time to be a descendant of the real Banquo, the story was altered so that Banquo was blameless. As far back as the Middle Ages, Kings were believed to have been chosen by God, and to emphasize the horror of what Macbeth does, King Duncan is portrayed as noble, rather than as the weak leader he was believed to have been. As Macbeth commits regicide (killing the King) it was necessary that he be seen to lose everything. King James I had written a paper called *Daemonologie* about the supernatural and it is the witches in the play who awaken Macbeth's ambition and tempt him into betraying his moral values, which eventually results in his death.

Where Shakespeare sourced his ideas

Shakespeare based his play on *Chronicles of Scotland* (1577) by Raphael Holinshed. He altered the story to flatter the King and to be more dramatically effective. Shakespeare only allows Macbeth to rule for a year whereas he ruled for 17 years. Songs were also added which are believed to be from Thomas Middleton's play *The Witch*, and Act III scene V where Hecate meets with the witches is believed to have been added after the play was complete. *Macbeth* was written in 1606 but was not published until 1623 in the first Folio of Shakespeare's Works. The play that you are reading and that is seen in theatres today would be quite different to the one shown to Shakespeare's audiences.

What it was like in England when Shakespeare wrote *Macbeth*

Macbeth is a tragedy that explores the darker side of human nature. This reflected the way that people in England were feeling at the time. King James VI of Scotland taking the throne of England when Queen Elizabeth I died caused great social unrest. He was not Queen Elizabeth I's descendant and therefore there were people who thought they had as much right to the throne as him. There was also religious unrest because King James I of England was a Protestant like Queen Elizabeth I, which made him an acceptable choice to many, but there was tension with the Catholic Church which resulted in conspiracies against King James I and parliament. It is believed that *Macbeth* was written at least in part as a warning about what happens to people who plot against the King.

Understanding the world of the play

It is important to understand the setting of the play and what life would have been like for the characters.

Macbeth is set in 11th Century Scotland where, although the King and government ruled, on a day to day basis Thanes oversaw the area where they lived. Thane was a title that was awarded to noblemen, and in the play Macbeth is awarded the title Thane of Cawdor because of his bravery in battle. As a piece of theatre, the heath where the witches tell Macbeth and Banquo the prophecies creates a mysterious and desolate setting, and Dunsinane Castle shows Macbeth's wealth and social position to the audience.

Women had absolutely no rights and were rarely even educated. This is important as in the play Lady Macbeth is power hungry and ambitious and asks the powers of evil to *"unsex her"* and to take away her feminine qualities so that she can be ruthless enough to convince Macbeth to murder the King. Lady Macbeth as the wife of a nobleman would have been well treated, however, she has no control over her own destiny.

INFORMATION ABOUT THE
KEY CHARACTERS

Shakespeare's characters are used to reveal his ideas and themes to the audience.

Macbeth
The main protagonist (character) who is a General in King Duncan's army. The witches' prophecy and his and his wife's ambition show what happens when he betrays his moral values and murders the King.

Lady Macbeth
Macbeth's wife who is even more ambitious for him than he is. She convinces him to murder King Duncan but is then shown to be unable to live with what she has done.

The Witches
Three "weird sisters" whose function is to tempt Macbeth and Banquo with their prophecies.

Banquo
A General in King Duncan's army and Macbeth's best friend. Although he receives a prophecy that his descendants will be Kings, he is shown to have the integrity not to act to make this happen.

King Duncan

The King of Scotland, who is presented as a worthy monarch and therefore Macbeth killing him is made to seem an even greater sin.

Malcolm

King Duncan's eldest son and heir to the throne who with Macduff's help overthrows Macbeth and takes the throne, showing him to be the rightful ruler of Scotland.

Macduff

A thane who is against Macbeth being made King and who helps King Duncan's son Malcolm to reclaim the throne.

Fleance

Banquo's young son who escapes when his father is murdered and who will become King if the witches' final prophecy comes true.

The Porter

The drunken doorman at Macbeth's Castle who directly addresses the audience. His speech provides brief comic relief from the events that have taken place.

It is important to realize that some of the characters might be regarded differently by an audience in Shakespeare's day. The witches would have been greatly feared and believed to have held greater knowledge than that of our world. Killing the King would have made the audience despise Macbeth and eagerly await his death.

SHAKESPEARE'S LANGUAGE

The language used in Shakespeare's plays is extremely important!

It is used to create a sense of time and place for the audience and to describe the setting, sound effects and atmosphere as well as signalling the characters' entrances and exits. It is also used to report action that has taken place off stage such as battles which it would not have been possible to show effectively as there were not the technical effects available that there are today.

The way in which characters in Shakespeare's plays speak is determined by the type of character they are and often their social class. The main protagonists and wealthy upper-class characters such as Macbeth and Lady Macbeth speak in Blank Verse. This is poetic language that is written in iambic pentameter. There are ten syllables in each line and five are stressed and five unstressed. This provides a regular rhythm in which the lines are delivered. Such characters perform soliloquies (written in Blank Verse) where they speak their thoughts aloud on stage for the audience to hear. Lower class or comedy characters such as the Porter speak in prose which does not have this poetic rhythm to it. The witches speak in rhyming couplets, making them seem more mysterious and different from the other characters.

The plotline of *Macbeth*

Act I

The play opens with a storm and sets up a mysterious and frightening atmosphere for the audience. Three witches plan to and later manage to intercept Macbeth and his friend Banquo on their way back from battle. They tell them three prophecies: that Macbeth will be Thane of Cawdor and then King and Banquo's descendants will be Kings, although he won't be. They dismiss the idea until Macbeth is made Thane of Cawdor for his bravery in battle and then he wonders if this has come true, then will the prophecy that he will be King come true as well? King Duncan names his son Malcolm as the heir to the throne and Macbeth writes to his wife about everything that has happened. When he arrives back at his castle, she convinces him to kill King Duncan who arrives to stay with them. Macbeth has his doubts, but she coerces him into committing the murder.

Act II

Banquo tells Macbeth that he dreamed about the witches and their prophecies, but Macbeth denies having thought about them and encourages Banquo to go to bed. He then sets about murdering the King. He returns to Lady Macbeth having murdered King Duncan and waits for the body to be discovered. The drunken porter pretends to guard the gates of Hell (allowing a brief break for the audience in the tension that is building) and Malcolm and Lennox find the body. Macbeth murders King Duncan's attendants in a state of panic and in fear of their lives Malcolm and Donalbain flee the country. It is decided that Macbeth shall become King.

Act III

Macbeth arranges to have Banquo and his son Fleance murdered by hired assassins as Banquo seems suspicious about King Duncan's murder and is potentially a threat to

Macbeth because of the prophecy that his descendants will be Kings rather than Macbeth's. The murderers kill Banquo but Fleance escapes. Macbeth holds a feast once he is crowned and Banquo's ghost appears, but only to him. He speaks to the ghost and the Lords at the feast are worried about his sanity. Macbeth decides to visit the witches to find out what is going to happen and meanwhile witches meet with their Queen, Hecate, and prepare for Macbeth's arrival. A thane called Lennox and a Lord discuss that Macduff is travelling to England to join Malcolm and that together they are raising an army to overthrow Macbeth.

Act IV

The witches meet with Macbeth and show him a series of visions which show further prophecies. He learns that he must beware of Macduff, but also that he cannot be killed by any man born of a woman and that he will be safe until Birnam Wood comes to Dunsinane Castle. He is reassured by this but when he learns that Macduff has left for England to join Malcolm, he has Macduff's family murdered. Macduff and Malcolm are planning their attack on Macbeth when they hear of the murders and Macduff vows revenge!

Act V

Lady Macbeth has gone insane from guilt at her part in King Duncan's murder. She sleepwalks and tries to wash the blood from her hands. Macbeth hears the army are advancing and tries to comfort himself with the witches' prophecies. He learns that his wife has killed herself and that the invading army are approaching Dunsinane Castle using the branches from Birnam Wood to shield them. He is confronted by Macduff who he is convinced cannot slay him until he hears that Macduff was born by caesarean section and therefore not technically born of woman. They exit fighting and Macduff kills Macbeth. Macduff returns and presents Macbeth's head to Malcolm who invites everyone to Scone to watch him be crowned.

CHARACTERS

DUNCAN, King of Scotland

MACBETH, Thane of Glamis and Cawdor, a general in the King's army

LADY MACBETH, his wife

MACDUFF, Thane of Fife, a nobleman of Scotland

LADY MACDUFF, his wife

MALCOLM, elder son of Duncan

DONALBAIN, younger son of Duncan

BANQUO, Thane of Lochaber, a general in the King's army

FLEANCE, his son

LENNOX, nobleman of Scotland

ROSS, nobleman of Scotland

MENTEITH, nobleman of Scotland

ANGUS, nobleman of Scotland

CAITHNESS, nobleman of Scotland

SIWARD, Earl of Northumberland, general of the English forces

YOUNG SIWARD, his son

SEYTON, attendant to Macbeth

HECATE, Queen of the Witches

The Three Witches

Boy, Son of Macduff

Gentlewoman attending on Lady Macbeth

An English Doctor
A Scottish Doctor
A Sergeant
A Porter
An Old Man
The Ghost of Banquo and other Apparitions
Lords, Gentlemen, Officers, Soldiers, Murderers, Attendants,
and Messengers

Settings: Scotland and England

ACT I

SCENE I

A deserted place. Thunder and lightning.

Enter three WITCHES.

FIRST WITCH
    When shall we three meet again?
    In thunder, lightning, or in rain?

SECOND WITCH
    When the hurlyburly's done,
    When the battle's lost and won.

THIRD WITCH
    That will be ere the set of sun.

FIRST WITCH
    Where the place?

SECOND WITCH
    Upon the heath.

THIRD WITCH
    There to meet with Macbeth.

FIRST WITCH
    I come, Graymalkin.

SECOND WITCH
    Paddock calls.

THIRD WITCH
    Anon!

ALL
    Fair is foul, and foul is fair.
    Hover through the fog and filthy air.

Exeunt.

SCENE II

A camp near Forres. Alarum within.

Enter DUNCAN, MALCOLM, DONALBAIN,
LENNOX, with ATTENDANTS, meeting a
bleeding SERGEANT.

DUNCAN
    What bloody man is that? He can report,
    As seemeth by his plight, of the revolt
    The newest state.

MALCOLM
    This is the sergeant
    Who like a good and hardy soldier fought
    'Gainst my captivity. Hail, brave friend!
    Say to the King the knowledge of the broil
    As thou didst leave it.

SERGEANT
    Doubtful it stood,
    As two spent swimmers that do cling together
    And choke their art. The merciless Macdonwald –
    Worthy to be a rebel, for to that
    The multiplying villainies of nature

Do swarm upon him – from the Western Isles
Of kerns and gallowglasses is supplied;
And Fortune, on his damned quarrel smiling,
Show'd like a rebel's whore. But all's too weak;
For brave Macbeth – well he deserves that name –
Disdaining Fortune, with his brandish'd steel,
Which smoked with bloody execution,
Like Valour's minion carved out his passage
Till he faced the slave,
Which ne'er shook hands, nor bade farewell to him,
Till he unseam'd him from the nave to the chaps,
And fix'd his head upon our battlements.

DUNCAN
O valiant cousin! Worthy gentleman!

SERGEANT
As whence the sun 'gins his reflection
Shipwrecking storms and direful thunders break,
So from that spring whence comfort seem'd
    to come
Discomfort swells. Mark, King of Scotland, mark.
No sooner justice had, with valour arm'd,
Compell'd these skipping kerns to trust their heels,
But the Norwegian lord, surveying vantage,
With furbish'd arms and new supplies of men,
Began a fresh assault.

DUNCAN
Dismay'd not this
Our captains, Macbeth and Banquo?

SERGEANT
Yes,
As sparrows eagles, or the hare the lion.
If I say sooth, I must report they were
As cannons overcharged with double cracks,
So they

Doubly redoubled strokes upon the foe.
Except they meant to bathe in reeking wounds,
Or memorize another Golgotha,
I cannot tell –
But I am faint; my gashes cry for help.

DUNCAN
So well thy words become thee as thy wounds;
They smack of honour both. Go get him surgeons.

Exit SERGEANT, *attended.*

Who comes here?

Enter ROSS.

MALCOLM
The worthy Thane of Ross.

LENNOX
What a haste looks through his eyes! So should he look
That seems to speak things strange.

ROSS
God save the King!

DUNCAN
Whence camest thou, worthy Thane?

ROSS
From Fife, great King,
Where the Norwegian banners flout the sky
And fan our people cold.
Norway himself, with terrible numbers,
Assisted by that most disloyal traitor
The Thane of Cawdor, began a dismal conflict,
Till that Bellona's bridegroom, lapp'd in proof,
Confronted him with self-comparisons,

Point against point rebellious, arm 'gainst arm,
Curbing his lavish spirit; and, to conclude,
The victory fell on us.

DUNCAN
Great happiness!

ROSS
That now Sweno,
the Norways' king, craves composition;
Nor would we deign him burial of his men
Till he disbursed, at Saint Colme's Inch,
Ten thousand dollars to our general use.

DUNCAN
No more that Thane of Cawdor shall deceive
Our bosom interest. Go pronounce his present death,
And with his former title greet Macbeth.

ROSS
I'll see it done.

DUNCAN
What he hath lost, noble Macbeth hath won.

Exeunt.

SCENE III

A heath. Thunder.

Enter the three WITCHES.

FIRST WITCH
Where hast thou been, sister?

SECOND WITCH
Killing swine.

THIRD WITCH
Sister, where thou?

FIRST WITCH
A sailor's wife had chestnuts in her lap,
And munch'd, and munch'd, and munch'd. "Give me,"
quoth I.
"Aroint thee, witch!" the rump-fed ronyon cries.
Her husband's to Aleppo gone, master the Tiger;
But in a sieve I'll thither sail,
And, like a rat without a tail,
I'll do, I'll do, and I'll do.

SECOND WITCH
I'll give thee a wind.

FIRST WITCH
Thou'rt kind.

THIRD WITCH
And I another.

FIRST WITCH
I myself have all the other,
And the very ports they blow,
All the quarters that they know
I' the shipman's card.
I will drain him dry as hay:
Sleep shall neither night nor day
Hang upon his penthouse lid;
He shall live a man forbid.
Weary se'nnights nine times nine
Shall he dwindle, peak, and pine;
Though his bark cannot be lost,
Yet it shall be tempest-toss'd.
Look what I have.

SECOND WITCH

  Show me, show me.

FIRST WITCH

  Here I have a pilot's thumb,
  Wreck'd as homeward he did come.

  Drum within.

THIRD WITCH

  A drum, a drum!
  Macbeth doth come.

ALL

  The weird sisters, hand in hand,
  Posters of the sea and land,
  Thus do go about, about,
  Thrice to thine, and thrice to mine,
  And thrice again, to make up nine.
  Peace! The charm's wound up.

Enter MACBETH and BANQUO.

MACBETH

  So foul and fair a day I have not seen.

BANQUO

  How far is't call'd to Forres? What are these
  So wither'd and so wild in their attire,
  That look not like the inhabitants o' the earth,
  And yet are on't? Live you? or are you aught
  That man may question? You seem to understand me,
  By each at once her choppy finger laying
  Upon her skinny lips. You should be women,
  And yet your beards forbid me to interpret
  That you are so.

MACBETH
Speak, if you can. What are you?

FIRST WITCH
All hail, Macbeth, hail to thee, Thane of Glamis!

SECOND WITCH
All hail, Macbeth, hail to thee, Thane of Cawdor!

THIRD WITCH
All hail, Macbeth, that shalt be King hereafter!

BANQUO
Good sir, why do you start, and seem to fear
Things that do sound so fair? I' the name of truth,
Are ye fantastical or that indeed
Which outwardly ye show? My noble partner
You greet with present grace and great prediction
Of noble having and of royal hope,
That he seems rapt withal. To me you speak not.
If you can look into the seeds of time,
And say which grain will grow and which will not,
Speak then to me, who neither beg nor fear
Your favours nor your hate.

FIRST WITCH
Hail!

SECOND WITCH
Hail!

THIRD WITCH
Hail!

FIRST WITCH
Lesser than Macbeth, and greater.

SECOND WITCH
Not so happy, yet much happier.

THIRD WITCH

Thou shalt get kings, though thou be none.
So all hail, Macbeth and Banquo!

FIRST WITCH

Banquo and Macbeth, all hail!

MACBETH

Stay, you imperfect speakers, tell me more.
By Sinel's death I know I am Thane of Glamis;
But how of Cawdor? The Thane of Cawdor lives,
A prosperous gentleman; and to be King
Stands not within the prospect of belief,
No more than to be Cawdor. Say from whence
You owe this strange intelligence, or why
Upon this blasted heath you stop our way
With such prophetic greeting? Speak, I charge you.

WITCHES *vanish*.

BANQUO

The earth hath bubbles as the water has,
And these are of them. Whither are they vanish'd?

MACBETH

Into the air, and what seem'd corporal melted
As breath into the wind. Would they had stay'd!

BANQUO

Were such things here as we do speak about?
Or have we eaten on the insane root
That takes the reason prisoner?

MACBETH

Your children shall be kings.

BANQUO

You shall be King.

MACBETH

And Thane of Cawdor too. Went it not so?

BANQUO

To the selfsame tune and words. Who's here?

Enter ROSS *and* ANGUS.

ROSS

The King hath happily received, Macbeth,
The news of thy success; and when he reads
Thy personal venture in the rebels' fight,
His wonders and his praises do contend
Which should be thine or his. Silenced with that,
In viewing o'er the rest o' the selfsame day,
He finds thee in the stout Norwegian ranks,
Nothing afeard of what thyself didst make,
Strange images of death. As thick as hail
Came post with post, and every one did bear
Thy praises in his kingdom's great defence,
And pour'd them down before him.

ANGUS

We are sent
To give thee, from our royal master, thanks;
Only to herald thee into his sight,
Not pay thee.

ROSS

And for an earnest of a greater honour,
He bade me, from him, call thee Thane of Cawdor.
In which addition, hail, most worthy Thane,
For it is thine.

BANQUO

What, can the devil speak true?

MACBETH
    The Thane of Cawdor lives. Why do you dress me
    In borrow'd robes?

ANGUS
    Who was the Thane lives yet,
    But under heavy judgement bears that life
    Which he deserves to lose. Whether he was combined
    With those of Norway, or did line the rebel
    With hidden help and vantage, or that with both
    He labour'd in his country's wreck, I know not;
    But treasons capital, confess'd and proved,
    Have overthrown him.

MACBETH
    [*Aside.*] Glamis, and Thane of Cawdor!
    The greatest is behind.
    [*To* ROSS *and* ANGUS] Thanks for your pains.
    [*Aside to* BANQUO] Do you not hope your children shall
    be kings,
    When those that gave the Thane of Cawdor to me
    Promised no less to them?

BANQUO
    [*Aside to* MACBETH.] That, trusted home,
    Might yet enkindle you unto the crown,
    Besides the Thane of Cawdor. But 'tis strange;
    And oftentimes, to win us to our harm,
    The instruments of darkness tell us truths,
    Win us with honest trifles, to betray's
    In deepest consequence –
    Cousins, a word, I pray you.

MACBETH
    [*Aside.*] Two truths are told,
    As happy prologues to the swelling act
    Of the imperial theme – I thank you, gentlemen.
    This supernatural soliciting

Cannot be ill, cannot be good. If ill,
Why hath it given me earnest of success,
Commencing in a truth? I am Thane of Cawdor.
If good, why do I yield to that suggestion
Whose horrid image doth unfix my hair
And make my seated heart knock at my ribs,
Against the use of nature? Present fears
Are less than horrible imaginings:
My thought, whose murder yet is but fantastical,
Shakes so my single state of man that function
Is smother'd in surmise, and nothing is
But what is not.

BANQUO

Look, how our partner's rapt.

MACBETH

[*Aside.*] If chance will have me King, why, chance may
crown me
Without my stir.

BANQUO

New honours come upon him,
Like our strange garments, cleave not to their mould
But with the aid of use.

MACBETH

[*Aside.*] Come what come may,
Time and the hour runs through the roughest day.

BANQUO

Worthy Macbeth, we stay upon your leisure.

MACBETH

Give me your favour; my dull brain was wrought
With things forgotten. Kind gentlemen, your pains
Are register'd where every day I turn
The leaf to read them. Let us toward the King.
Think upon what hath chanced, and at more time,

The interim having weigh'd it, let us speak
Our free hearts each to other.

BANQUO
Very gladly.

MACBETH
Till then, enough. Come, friends.

Exeunt.

SCENE IV

Forres. King Duncan's palace.
Flourish.

Enter DUNCAN, MALCOLM, DONALBAIN, LENNOX,
and ATTENDANTS.

DUNCAN
Is execution done on Cawdor? Are not
Those in commission yet return'd?

MALCOLM
My liege,
They are not yet come back. But I have spoke
With one that saw him die, who did report
That very frankly he confess'd his treasons,
Implored your Highness' pardon, and set forth
A deep repentance. Nothing in his life
Became him like the leaving it; he died
As one that had been studied in his death,
To throw away the dearest thing he owed
As 'twere a careless trifle.

DUNCAN

There's no art
To find the mind's construction in the face:
He was a gentleman on whom I built
An absolute trust.

Enter MACBETH, BANQUO, ROSS, *and* ANGUS.

O worthiest cousin!
The sin of my ingratitude even now
Was heavy on me. Thou art so far before,
That swiftest wing of recompense is slow
To overtake thee. Would thou hadst less deserved,
That the proportion both of thanks and payment
Might have been mine! Only I have left to say,
More is thy due than more than all can pay.

MACBETH

The service and the loyalty I owe,
In doing it, pays itself. Your Highness' part
Is to receive our duties, and our duties
Are to your throne and state, children and servants,
Which do but what they should, by doing everything
Safe toward your love and honour.

DUNCAN

Welcome hither.
I have begun to plant thee, and will labour
To make thee full of growing. Noble Banquo,
That hast no less deserved, nor must be known
No less to have done so; let me enfold thee
And hold thee to my heart.

BANQUO

There if I grow,
The harvest is your own.

DUNCAN

My plenteous joys,
Wanton in fullness, seek to hide themselves
In drops of sorrow. Sons, kinsmen, thanes,
And you whose places are the nearest, know
We will establish our estate upon
Our eldest, Malcolm, whom we name hereafter
The Prince of Cumberland; which honour must
Not unaccompanied invest him only,
But signs of nobleness, like stars, shall shine
On all deservers. From hence to Inverness,
And bind us further to you.

MACBETH

The rest is labour, which is not used for you.
I'll be myself the harbinger, and make joyful
The hearing of my wife with your approach;
So humbly take my leave.

DUNCAN

My worthy Cawdor!

MACBETH

[*Aside.*] The Prince of Cumberland! That is a step
On which I must fall down, or else o'erleap,
For in my way it lies. Stars, hide your fires;
Let not light see my black and deep desires.
The eye wink at the hand; yet let that be
Which the eye fears, when it is done, to see.

Exit.

DUNCAN

True, worthy Banquo! He is full so valiant,
And in his commendations I am fed;
It is a banquet to me. Let's after him,
Whose care is gone before to bid us welcome.

It is a peerless kinsman.

Flourish. Exeunt.

SCENE V

Inverness. Macbeth's castle.

Enter LADY MACBETH, *reading a letter.*

LADY MACBETH
"They met me in the day of success, and I have learned
by the perfectest report they have more in them than
mortal knowledge. When I burned in desire to question
them further, they made themselves air, into which they
vanished. Whiles I stood rapt in the wonder of it, came
missives from the King, who all-hailed me 'Thane of
Cawdor'; by which title, before, these weird sisters saluted
me and referred me to the coming on of time with 'Hail,
King that shalt be!' This have I thought good to deliver
thee, my dearest partner of greatness, that thou mightst
not lose the dues of rejoicing, by being ignorant of what
greatness is promised thee. Lay it to thy heart, and
farewell."
Glamis thou art, and Cawdor, and shalt be
What thou art promised. Yet do I fear thy nature.
It is too full o' the milk of human kindness
To catch the nearest way. Thou wouldst be great;
Art not without ambition, but without
The illness should attend it. What thou wouldst highly,
That wouldst thou holily; wouldst not play false,
And yet wouldst wrongly win. Thou'ldst have, great Glamis,
That which cries, "Thus thou must do, if thou have it;

And that which rather thou dost fear to do
Than wishest should be undone." Hie thee hither,
That I may pour my spirits in thine ear,
And chastise with the valour of my tongue
All that impedes thee from the golden round,
Which fate and metaphysical aid doth seem
To have thee crown'd withal.

Enter a MESSENGER.

What is your tidings?

MESSENGER
The King comes here tonight.

LADY MACBETH
Thou'rt mad to say it!
Is not thy master with him? who, were't so,
Would have inform'd for preparation.

MESSENGER
So please you, it is true; our Thane is coming.
One of my fellows had the speed of him,
Who, almost dead for breath, had scarcely more
Than would make up his message.

LADY MACBETH
Give him tending;
He brings great news.

Exit MESSENGER.

The raven himself is hoarse
That croaks the fatal entrance of Duncan
Under my battlements. Come, you spirits
That tend on mortal thoughts, unsex me here
And fill me from the crown to the toe top – full
Of direst cruelty! Make thick my blood,

Stop up the access and passage to remorse,
That no compunctious visitings of nature
Shake my fell purpose nor keep peace between
The effect and it! Come to my woman's breasts,
And take my milk for gall, your murdering
    ministers,
Wherever in your sightless substances
You wait on nature's mischief! Come, thick night,
And pall thee in the dunnest smoke of hell
That my keen knife see not the wound it makes
Nor heaven peep through the blanket of the dark
To cry, "Hold, hold!"

Enter MACBETH.

Great Glamis! Worthy Cawdor!
Greater than both, by the all-hail hereafter!
Thy letters have transported me beyond
This ignorant present, and I feel now
The future in the instant.

MACBETH
My dearest love,
Duncan comes here tonight.

LADY MACBETH
And when goes hence?

MACBETH
Tomorrow, as he purposes.

LADY MACBETH
O, never
Shall sun that morrow see!
Your face, my Thane, is as a book where men
May read strange matters. To beguile the time,
Look like the time; bear welcome in your eye,
Your hand, your tongue; look like the innocent flower,

But be the serpent under it. He that's coming
Must be provided for; and you shall put
This night's great business into my dispatch,
Which shall to all our nights and days to come
Give solely sovereign sway and masterdom.

MACBETH
We will speak further.

LADY MACBETH
Only look up clear;
To alter favour ever is to fear.
Leave all the rest to me.

Exeunt.

SCENE VI

Before Macbeth's castle. Hautboys and torches.

Enter DUNCAN, MALCOLM, DONALBAIN, BANQUO,
LENNOX, MACDUFF, ROSS, ANGUS, *and* ATTENDANTS.

DUNCAN
This castle hath a pleasant seat; the air
Nimbly and sweetly recommends itself
Unto our gentle senses.

BANQUO
This guest of summer,
The temple-haunting martlet, does approve
By his loved mansionry that the heaven's breath
Smells wooingly here. No jutty, frieze,
Buttress, nor coign of vantage, but this bird
Hath made his pendant bed and procreant cradle;

Where they most breed and haunt, I have observed
The air is delicate.

Enter LADY MACBETH.

DUNCAN
See, see, our honour'd hostess!
The love that follows us sometime is our trouble,
Which still we thank as love. Herein I teach you
How you shall bid God yield us for your pains,
And thank us for your trouble.

LADY MACBETH
All our service
In every point twice done, and then done double,
Were poor and single business to contend
Against those honours deep and broad wherewith
Your Majesty loads our house. For those of old,
And the late dignities heap'd up to them,
We rest your hermits.

DUNCAN
Where's the Thane of Cawdor?
We coursed him at the heels and had a purpose
To be his purveyor; but he rides well,
And his great love, sharp as his spur, hath holp him
To his home before us. Fair and noble hostess,
We are your guest tonight.

LADY MACBETH
Your servants ever
Have theirs, themselves, and what is theirs, in compt,
To make their audit at your Highness' pleasure,
Still to return your own.

DUNCAN
Give me your hand;

Conduct me to mine host. We love him highly,
And shall continue our graces towards him.
By your leave, hostess.

Exeunt.

SCENE VII

Macbeth's castle. Hautboys and torches.

Enter a SEWER *and divers* SERVANTS *with dishes and service, who pass over the stage. Then enter* MACBETH.

MACBETH
    If it were done when 'tis done, then 'twere well
    It were done quickly. If the assassination
    Could trammel up the consequence, and catch,
    With his surcease, success; that but this blow
    Might be the be-all and the end-all – here,
    But here, upon this bank and shoal of time,
    We'd jump the life to come. But in these cases
    We still have judgement here, that we but teach
    Bloody instructions, which being taught return
    To plague the inventor. This even-handed justice
    Commends the ingredients of our poison'd chalice
    To our own lips. He's here in double trust:
    First, as I am his kinsman and his subject,
    Strong both against the deed; then, as his host,
    Who should against his murderer shut the door,
    Not bear the knife myself. Besides, this Duncan
    Hath borne his faculties so meek, hath been
    So clear in his great office, that his virtues
    Will plead like angels trumpet-tongued against

The deep damnation of his taking-off,
And pity, like a naked new-born babe
Striding the blast, or heaven's cherubin horsed
Upon the sightless couriers of the air,
Shall blow the horrid deed in every eye,
That tears shall drown the wind. I have no spur
To prick the sides of my intent, but only
Vaulting ambition, which o'erleaps itself
And falls on the other.

Enter LADY MACBETH.

How now, what news?

LADY MACBETH
He has almost supp'd. Why have you left the chamber?

MACBETH
Hath he ask'd for me?

LADY MACBETH
Know you not he has?

MACBETH
We will proceed no further in this business:
He hath honour'd me of late, and I have bought
Golden opinions from all sorts of people,
Which would be worn now in their newest gloss,
Not cast aside so soon.

LADY MACBETH
Was the hope drunk
Wherein you dress'd yourself? Hath it slept since?
And wakes it now, to look so green and pale
At what it did so freely? From this time
Such I account thy love. Art thou afeard
To be the same in thine own act and valour
As thou art in desire? Wouldst thou have that

Which thou esteem'st the ornament of life
And live a coward in thine own esteem,
Letting "I dare not" wait upon "I would"
Like the poor cat i' the adage?

MACBETH
Prithee, peace!
I dare do all that may become a man;
Who dares do more is none.

LADY MACBETH
What beast was't then
That made you break this enterprise to me?
When you durst do it, then you were a man,
And, to be more than what you were, you would
Be so much more the man. Nor time nor place
Did then adhere, and yet you would make both.
They have made themselves, and that their
   fitness now
Does unmake you. I have given suck and know
How tender 'tis to love the babe that milks me –
I would, while it was smiling in my face,
Have pluck'd my nipple from his boneless gums
And dash'd the brains out had I so sworn as you
Have done to this.

MACBETH
If we should fail?

LADY MACBETH
We fail?
But screw your courage to the sticking-place
And we'll not fail. When Duncan is asleep –
Whereto the rather shall his day's hard journey
Soundly invite him – his two chamberlains
Will I with wine and wassail so convince
That memory, the warder of the brain,
Shall be a fume and the receipt of reason

A limbeck only. When in swinish sleep
Their drenched natures lie as in a death,
What cannot you and I perform upon
The unguarded Duncan? What not put upon
His spongy officers, who shall bear the guilt
Of our great quell?

MACBETH

Bring forth men-children only,
For thy undaunted mettle should compose
Nothing but males. Will it not be received,
When we have mark'd with blood those sleepy two
Of his own chamber and used their very daggers,
That they have done't?

LADY MACBETH

Who dares receive it other,
As we shall make our griefs and clamour roar
Upon his death?

MACBETH

I am settled and bend up
Each corporal agent to this terrible feat.
Away, and mock the time with fairest show:
False face must hide what the false heart doth know.

Exeunt.

ACT II

SCENE I

Inverness. Court of Macbeth's castle.

Enter BANQUO *and* FLEANCE, *bearing a torch before him.*

BANQUO
How goes the night, boy?

FLEANCE
The moon is down; I have not heard the clock.

BANQUO
And she goes down at twelve.

FLEANCE
I take't 'tis later, sir.

BANQUO
Hold, take my sword. There's husbandry in heaven,
Their candles are all out. Take thee that too.
A heavy summons lies like lead upon me,
And yet I would not sleep. Merciful powers,
Restrain in me the cursed thoughts that nature
Gives way to in repose!

Enter MACBETH *and a* SERVANT *with a torch.*

Give me my sword.
Who's there?

39

MACBETH

A friend.

BANQUO

What, sir, not yet at rest? The King's abed.
He hath been in unusual pleasure and
Sent forth great largess to your offices.
This diamond he greets your wife withal,
By the name of most kind hostess, and shut up
In measureless content.

MACBETH

Being unprepared,
Our will became the servant to defect,
Which else should free have wrought.

BANQUO

All's well.
I dreamt last night of the three weird sisters:
To you they have show'd some truth.

MACBETH

I think not of them;
Yet, when we can entreat an hour to serve,
We would spend it in some words upon that business,
If you would grant the time.

BANQUO

At your kind'st leisure.

MACBETH

If you shall cleave to my consent, when 'tis,
It shall make honour for you.

BANQUO

So I lose none
In seeking to augment it, but still keep
My bosom franchised and allegiance clear,
I shall be counsell'd.

MACBETH

Good repose the while.

BANQUO

Thanks, sir, the like to you.

Exeunt BANQUO *and* FLEANCE.

MACBETH

Go bid thy mistress, when my drink is ready,
She strike upon the bell. Get thee to bed.

Exit SERVANT.

Is this a dagger which I see before me,
The handle toward my hand? Come, let me clutch thee.
I have thee not, and yet I see thee still.
Art thou not, fatal vision, sensible
To feeling as to sight? Or art thou but
A dagger of the mind, a false creation,
Proceeding from the heat-oppressed brain?
I see thee yet, in form as palpable
As this which now I draw.
Thou marshal'st me the way that I was going,
And such an instrument I was to use.
Mine eyes are made the fools o' the other senses,
Or else worth all the rest. I see thee still,
And on thy blade and dudgeon gouts of blood,
Which was not so before. There's no such thing:
It is the bloody business which informs
Thus to mine eyes. Now o'er the one half-world
Nature seems dead, and wicked dreams abuse
The curtain'd sleep; witchcraft celebrates
Pale Hecate's offerings; and wither'd Murder,
Alarum'd by his sentinel, the wolf,
Whose howl's his watch, thus with his stealthy pace,

With Tarquin's ravishing strides, towards his design
Moves like a ghost. Thou sure and firm-set earth,
Hear not my steps, which way they walk, for fear
Thy very stones prate of my whereabout,
And take the present horror from the time,
Which now suits with it. Whiles I threat, he lives;
Words to the heat of deeds too cold breath gives.

A bell rings.

I go, and it is done; the bell invites me.
Hear it not, Duncan, for it is a knell
That summons thee to heaven, or to hell.

Exit.

SCENE II

Inverness. Court of Macbeth's castle.

Enter LADY MACBETH.

LADY MACBETH
That which hath made them drunk hath made me bold;
What hath quench'd them hath given me fire. Hark! Peace!
It was the owl that shriek'd, the fatal bellman,
Which gives the stern'st good night. He is about it:
The doors are open, and the surfeited grooms
Do mock their charge with snores. I have drugg'd their possets
That death and nature do contend about them,
Whether they live or die.

MACBETH

[*Within.*] Who's there' what, ho!

LADY MACBETH

Alack, I am afraid they have awaked
And 'tis not done. The attempt and not the deed
Confounds us. Hark! I laid their daggers ready;
He could not miss 'em. Had he not resembled
My father as he slept, I had done't.

Enter MACBETH.

My husband!

MACBETH

I have done the deed. Didst thou not hear a noise?

LADY MACBETH

I heard the owl scream and the crickets cry.
Did not you speak?

MACBETH

When?

LADY MACBETH

Now.

MACBETH

As I descended?

LADY MACBETH

Ay.

MACBETH

Hark!
Who lies i' the second chamber?

LADY MACBETH

Donalbain.

MACBETH

This is a sorry sight. [*Looks at his hands.*]

LADY MACBETH

A foolish thought, to say a sorry sight.

MACBETH

There's one did laugh in 's sleep, and one cried,
"Murder!"
That they did wake each other. I stood and heard them,
But they did say their prayers and address'd them
Again to sleep.

LADY MACBETH

There are two lodged together.

MACBETH

One cried, "God bless us!" and "Amen" the other,
As they had seen me with these hangman's hands.
Listening their fear, I could not say "Amen,"
When they did say, "God bless us!"

LADY MACBETH

Consider it not so deeply.

MACBETH

But wherefore could not I pronounce "Amen"?
I had most need of blessing, and "Amen"
Stuck in my throat.

LADY MACBETH

These deeds must not be thought
After these ways; so, it will make us mad.

MACBETH

I heard a voice cry, "Sleep no more!
Macbeth does murder sleep" – the innocent sleep,
Sleep that knits up the ravell'd sleave of care,
The death of each day's life, sore labour's bath,
Balm of hurt minds, great nature's second course,

44

Chief nourisher in life's feast –

LADY MACBETH
What do you mean?

MACBETH
Still it cried, "Sleep no more!" to all the house;
"Glamis hath murder'd sleep, and therefore Cawdor
Shall sleep no more. Macbeth shall sleep no more."

LADY MACBETH
Who was it that thus cried? Why, worthy Thane,
You do unbend your noble strength, to think
So brainsickly of things. Go, get some water
And wash this filthy witness from your hand.
Why did you bring these daggers from the place?
They must lie there. Go carry them, and smear
The sleepy grooms with blood.

MACBETH
I'll go no more.
I am afraid to think what I have done;
Look on't again I dare not.

LADY MACBETH
Infirm of purpose!
Give me the daggers. The sleeping and the dead
Are but as pictures; 'tis the eye of childhood
That fears a painted devil. If he do bleed,
I'll gild the faces of the grooms withal,
For it must seem their guilt.

Exit.

Knocking within.

MACBETH
Whence is that knocking?
How is't with me, when every noise appals me?

What hands are here? Ha, they pluck out mine
    eyes!
Will all great Neptune's ocean wash this blood
Clean from my hand? No, this my hand will rather
The multitudinous seas incarnadine,
Making the green one red.

Re-enter LADY MACBETH.

LADY MACBETH
    My hands are of your colour, but I shame
    To wear a heart so white. [*Knocking within.*] I hear
    knocking
    At the south entry. Retire we to our chamber.
    A little water clears us of this deed.
    How easy is it then! Your constancy
    Hath left you unattended. [*Knocking within.*] Hark, more
    knocking.
    Get on your nightgown, lest occasion call us
    And show us to be watchers. Be not lost
    So poorly in your thoughts.

MACBETH
    To know my deed, 'twere best not know myself.

Knocking within.

Wake Duncan with thy knocking! I would thou couldst!

Exeunt

SCENE III

Inverness. Court of Macbeth's castle.

Enter a PORTER.

Knocking within.

PORTER
Here's a knocking indeed! If a man were porter of Hell
Gate, he should have old turning the key.
[*Knocking within.*] Knock, knock, knock! Who's there, i' the
name of Belzebub?
Here's a farmer that hanged himself on th' expectation of
plenty. Come in time!
Have napkins enough about you; here you'll sweat fort.
[*Knocking within.*] Knock, knock! Who's there, in th' other
devil's name?
Faith, here's an equivocator that could swear in both the
scales against either scale, who committed treason enough
for God's sake, yet could not equivocate to heaven. O, come
in, equivocator.
[*Knocking within.*] Knock, knock, knock!
Who's there? Faith, here's an English tailor come hither, for
stealing out of a French hose. Come in, tailor; here you may
roast your goose.
[*Knocking within.*] Knock, knock! Never at quiet! What are
you? But this place is too cold for hell. I'll devil-porter it no
further. I had thought to have let in some of all professions,
that go the primrose way to the everlasting bonfire.
[*Knocking within.*] Anon, anon! I pray you, remember the
porter.

Opens the gate.

Enter MACDUFF *and* LENNOX.

MACDUFF
Was it so late, friend, ere you went to bed,

47

That you do lie so late?

PORTER

Faith, sir, we were carousing till the second cock; and
drink, sir, is a great provoker of three things.

MACDUFF

What three things does drink especially provoke?

PORTER

Marry, sir, nose-painting, sleep, and urine. Lechery, sir,
it provokes and unprovokes: it provokes the desire, but it
takes away the performance.
Therefore much drink may be said to be an equivocator
with lechery: it makes him, and it mars him; it sets him
on, and it takes him off; it persuades him and disheartens
him; makes him stand to and not stand to; in conclusion,
equivocates him in a sleep, and giving him the lie, leaves
him.

MACDUFF

I believe drink gave thee the lie last night.

PORTER

That it did, sir, i' the very throat on me; but requited him
for his lie, and, I think, being too strong for him, though he
took up my legs sometime, yet I made shift to cast him.

MACDUFF

Is thy master stirring?

Enter MACBETH.

Our knocking has awaked him; here he comes.

LENNOX

Good morrow, noble sir.

MACBETH

Good morrow, both.

MACDUFF

Is the King stirring, worthy Thane?

MACBETH

Not yet.

MACDUFF

He did command me to call timely on him;
I have almost slipp'd the hour.

MACBETH

I'll bring you to him.

MACDUFF

I know this is a joyful trouble to you,
But yet 'tis one.

MACBETH

The labour we delight in physics pain.
This is the door.

MACDUFF

I'll make so bold to call,
For 'tis my limited service.

Exit.

LENNOX

Goes the King hence today?

MACBETH

He does; he did appoint so.

LENNOX

The night has been unruly. Where we lay,
Our chimneys were blown down, and, as they say,
Lamentings heard i' the air, strange screams
    of death,
And prophesying with accents terrible
Of dire combustion and confused events

New hatch'd to the woeful time. The obscure bird
Clamour'd the livelong night. Some say the earth
Was feverous and did shake.

MACBETH
'Twas a rough night.

LENNOX
My young remembrance cannot parallel
A fellow to it.

Re-enter MACDUFF.

MACDUFF
O horror, horror, horror! Tongue nor heart
Cannot conceive nor name thee.

MACBETH and LENNOX
What's the matter?

MACDUFF
Confusion now hath made his masterpiece.
Most sacrilegious murder hath broke ope
The Lord's anointed temple and stole thence
The life o' the building.

MACBETH
What is't you say? the life?

LENNOX
Mean you his Majesty?

MACDUFF
Approach the chamber, and destroy your sight
With a new Gorgon. Do not bid me speak;
See, and then speak yourselves.

Exeunt MACBETH *and* LENNOX.

Awake, awake!
Ring the alarum bell. Murder and treason!
Banquo and Donalbain! Malcolm, awake!
Shake off this downy sleep, death's counterfeit,
And look on death itself! Up, up, and see
The great doom's image! Malcolm! Banquo!
As from your graves rise up, and walk like sprites
To countenance this horror! Ring the bell. [*Bell rings.*]

Enter LADY MACBETH.

LADY MACBETH
What's the business,
That such a hideous trumpet calls to parley
The sleepers of the house? Speak, speak!

MACDUFF
O gentle lady,
'Tis not for you to hear what I can speak:
The repetition in a woman's ear
Would murder as it fell.

Enter BANQUO.

O Banquo, Banquo!
Our royal master's murder'd.

LADY MACBETH
Woe, alas!
What, in our house?

BANQUO
Too cruel anywhere.
Dear Duff, I prithee, contradict thyself,
And say it is not so.

Re-enter MACBETH *and* LENNOX, *with* ROSS.

MACBETH

Had I but died an hour before this chance,
I had lived a blessed time, for from this instant
There's nothing serious in mortality.
All is but toys; renown and grace is dead,
The wine of life is drawn, and the mere lees
Is left this vault to brag of.

Enter MALCOLM *and* DONALBAIN.

DONALBAIN

What is amiss?

MACBETH

You are, and do not know't.
The spring, the head, the fountain of your blood
Is stopped, the very source of it is stopp'd.

MACDUFF

Your royal father's murder'd.

MALCOLM

O, by whom?

LENNOX

Those of his chamber, as it seem'd, had done't.
Their hands and faces were all badged with blood;
So were their daggers, which unwiped we found
Upon their pillows.
They stared, and were distracted; no man's life
Was to be trusted with them.

MACBETH

O, yet I do repent me of my fury,
That I did kill them.

MACDUFF

Wherefore did you so?

MACBETH
Who can be wise, amazed, temperate and furious,
Loyal and neutral, in a moment? No man.
The expedition of my violent love
Outrun the pauser reason. Here lay Duncan,
His silver skin laced with his golden blood,
And his gash'd stabs look'd like a breach in nature
For ruin's wasteful entrance; there, the murderers,
Steep'd in the colours of their trade, their daggers
Unmannerly breech'd with gore. Who could refrain,
That had a heart to love, and in that heart
Courage to make 's love known?

LADY MACBETH
Help me hence, ho!

MACDUFF
Look to the lady.

MALCOLM
[*Aside to* DONALBAIN.] Why do we hold our tongues,
That most may claim this argument for ours?

DONALBAIN
[*Aside to* MALCOLM.] What should be spoken here,
where our fate,
Hid in an auger hole, may rush and seize us?
Let's away,
Our tears are not yet brew'd.

MALCOLM
[*Aside to* DONALBAIN.] Nor our strong sorrow
Upon the foot of motion.

BANQUO
Look to the lady.

LADY MACBETH *is carried out.*

And when we have our naked frailties hid,
That suffer in exposure, let us meet
And question this most bloody piece of work
To know it further. Fears and scruples shake us.
In the great hand of God I stand, and thence
Against the undivulged pretense I fight
Of treasonous malice.

MACDUFF
And so do I.

ALL
So all.

MACBETH
Let's briefly put on manly readiness
And meet i' the hall together.

ALL
Well contented.

Exeunt all but MALCOLM *and* DONALBAIN.

MALCOLM
What will you do? Let's not consort with them.
To show an unfelt sorrow is an office
Which the false man does easy. I'll to England.

DONALBAIN
To Ireland, I; our separated fortune
Shall keep us both the safer. Where we are
There's daggers in men's smiles; the near in blood,
The nearer bloody.

MALCOLM
This murderous shaft that's shot
Hath not yet lighted, and our safest way
Is to avoid the aim. Therefore to horse;
And let us not be dainty of leave-taking,

But shift away. There's warrant in that theft
Which steals itself when there's no mercy left.

Exeunt.

SCENE IV

Outside Macbeth's castle.

Enter ROSS *with an* OLD MAN.

OLD MAN
Threescore and ten I can remember well,
Within the volume of which time I have seen
Hours dreadful and things strange, but this sore night
Hath trifled former knowings.

ROSS
Ah, good father,
Thou seest the heavens, as troubled with man's act,
Threaten his bloody stage. By the clock 'tis day,
And yet dark night strangles the travelling lamp.
Is't night's predominance, or the day's shame,
That darkness does the face of earth entomb,
When living light should kiss it?

OLD MAN
'Tis unnatural,
Even like the deed that's done. On Tuesday last
A falcon towering in her pride of place
Was by a mousing owl hawk'd at and kill'd.

ROSS
And Duncan's horses – a thing most strange and certain –
Beauteous and swift, the minions of their race,

Turn'd wild in nature, broke their stalls, flung out,
Contending 'gainst obedience, as they would make
War with mankind.

OLD MAN

'Tis said they eat each other.

ROSS

They did so, to the amazement of mine eyes
That look'd upon't.

Enter MACDUFF.

Here comes the good Macduff.
How goes the world, sir, now?

MACDUFF

Why, see you not?

ROSS

Is't known who did this more than bloody deed?

MACDUFF

Those that Macbeth hath slain.

ROSS

Alas, the day!
What good could they pretend?

MACDUFF

They were suborn'd:
Malcolm and Donalbain, the King's two sons,
Are stol'n away and fled, which puts upon them
Suspicion of the deed.

ROSS

'Gainst nature still!
Thriftless ambition, that wilt ravin up
Thine own life's means! Then 'tis most like
The sovereignty will fall upon Macbeth.

MACDUFF

He is already named, and gone to Scone
To be invested.

ROSS

Where is Duncan's body?

MACDUFF

Carried to Colmekill,
The sacred storehouse of his predecessors
And guardian of their bones.

ROSS

Will you to Scone?

MACDUFF

No, cousin, I'll to Fife.

ROSS

Well, I will thither.

MACDUFF

Well, may you see things well done there.
Adieu,
Lest our old robes sit easier than our new!

ROSS

Farewell, father.

OLD MAN

God's benison go with you and with those
That would make good of bad and friends of foes!

Exeunt.

ACT III

SCENE I

Forres. The palace.

Enter BANQUO.

BANQUO
Thou hast it now: King, Cawdor, Glamis, all,
As the weird women promised, and I fear
Thou play'dst most foully for't; yet it was said
It should not stand in thy posterity,
But that myself should be the root and father
Of many kings. If there come truth from them
(As upon thee, Macbeth, their speeches shine)
Why, by the verities on thee made good,
May they not be my oracles as well
And set me up in hope? But hush, no more.

Sennet sounds. Enter MACBETH *as King,* LADY MACBETH
as Queen, LENNOX, ROSS, LORDS, LADIES, *and*
ATTENDANTS.

MACBETH
Here's our chief guest.

LADY MACBETH
If he had been forgotten,
It had been as a gap in our great feast
And all thing unbecoming.

MACBETH

Tonight we hold a solemn supper, sir,
And I'll request your presence.

BANQUO

Let your Highness
Command upon me, to the which my duties
Are with a most indissoluble tie
Forever knit.

MACBETH

Ride you this afternoon?

BANQUO

Ay, my good lord.

MACBETH

We should have else desired your good advice,
Which still hath been both grave and prosperous
In this day's council; but we'll take tomorrow.
Is't far you ride?

BANQUO

As far, my lord, as will fill up the time
'Twixt this and supper. Go not my horse the better,
I must become a borrower of the night
For a dark hour or twain.

MACBETH

Fail not our feast.

BANQUO

My lord, I will not.

MACBETH

We hear our bloody cousins are bestow'd
In England and in Ireland, not confessing
Their cruel parricide, filling their hearers
With strange invention. But of that tomorrow,
When therewithal we shall have cause of state

Craving us jointly. Hie you to horse; adieu,
Till you return at night. Goes Fleance with you?

BANQUO
Ay, my good lord. Our time does call upon 's.

MACBETH
I wish your horses swift and sure of foot,
And so I do commend you to their backs.
Farewell.

Exit BANQUO.

Let every man be master of his time
Till seven at night; to make society
The sweeter welcome, we will keep ourself
Till supper time alone. While then, God be with you!

Exeunt all but MACBETH *and an* ATTENDANT.

Sirrah, a word with you. Attend those men
Our pleasure?

ATTENDANT
They are, my lord, without the palace gate.

MACBETH
Bring them before us.

Exit ATTENDANT.

To be thus is nothing,
But to be safely thus. Our fears in Banquo.
Stick deep, and in his royalty of nature
Reigns that which would be fear'd. 'Tis much he dares,
And, to that dauntless temper of his mind,
He hath a wisdom that doth guide his valour
To act in safety. There is none but he

61

Whose being I do fear; and under him
My genius is rebuked, as it is said
Mark Antony's was by Caesar. He chid the sisters
When first they put the name of King upon me
And bade them speak to him; then prophet – like
They hail'd him father to a line of kings.
Upon my head they placed a fruitless crown
And put a barren sceptre in my gripe,
Thence to be wrench'd with an unlineal hand,
No son of mine succeeding. If't be so,
For Banquo's issue have I filled my mind,
For them the gracious Duncan have I murder'd,
Put rancours in the vessel of my peace
Only for them, and mine eternal jewel
Given to the common enemy of man,
To make them kings – the seed of Banquo kings!
Rather than so, come, Fate, into the list,
And champion me to the utterance! Who's there?

Re-enter ATTENDANT, *with two* MURDERERS.

Now go to the door, and stay there till we call.

Exit ATTENDANT.

Was it not yesterday we spoke together?

FIRST MURDERER
It was, so please your Highness.

MACBETH
Well then, now
Have you consider'd of my speeches? Know
That it was he in the times past which held you
So under fortune, which you thought had been
Our innocent self? This I made good to you
In our last conference, pass'd in probation with you:

62

How you were borne in hand, how cross'd, the instruments,
Who wrought with them, and all things else that might
To half a soul and to a notion crazed
Say, "Thus did Banquo."

FIRST MURDERER
You made it known to us.

MACBETH
I did so, and went further, which is now
Our point of second meeting. Do you find
Your patience so predominant in your nature,
That you can let this go? Are you so gospell'd,
To pray for this good man and for his issue,
Whose heavy hand hath bow'd you to the grave
And beggar'd yours forever?

FIRST MURDERER
We are men, my liege.

MACBETH
Ay, in the catalogue ye go for men,
As hounds and greyhounds, mongrels, spaniels, curs,
Shoughs, waterrugs, and demi-wolves are clept
All by the name of dogs. The valued file
Distinguishes the swift, the slow, the subtle,
The housekeeper, the hunter, every one
According to the gift which bounteous nature
Hath in him closed, whereby he does receive
Particular addition, from the bill
That writes them all alike; and so of men.
Now if you have a station in the file,
Not i' the worst rank of manhood, say it,
And I will put that business in your bosoms
Whose execution takes your enemy off,
Grapples you to the heart and love of us,
Who wear our health but sickly in his life,
Which in his death were perfect.

SECOND MURDERER
    I am one, my liege,
    Whom the vile blows and buffets of the world
    Have so incensed that I am reckless what
    I do to spite the world.

FIRST MURDERER
    And I another
    So weary with disasters, tugg'd with fortune,
    That I would set my life on any chance,
    To mend it or be rid on't.

MACBETH
    Both of you
    Know Banquo was your enemy.

BOTH MURDERERS
    True, my lord.

MACBETH
    So is he mine, and in such bloody distance
    That every minute of his being thrusts
    Against my near'st of life; and though I could
    With barefaced power sweep him from my sight
    And bid my will avouch it, yet I must not,
    For certain friends that are both his and mine,
    Whose loves I may not drop, but wail his fall
    Who I myself struck down. And thence it is
    That I to your assistance do make love,
    Masking the business from the common eye
    For sundry weighty reasons.

SECOND MURDERER
    We shall, my lord,
    Perform what you command us.

FIRST MURDERER
    Though our lives –

MACBETH

Your spirits shine through you. Within this hour at most
I will advise you where to plant yourselves,
Acquaint you with the perfect spy o' the time,
The moment on't; fort must be done tonight
And something from the palace (always thought
That I require a clearness); and with him –
To leave no rubs nor botches in the work –
Fleance his son, that keeps him company,
Whose absence is no less material to me
Than is his father's, must embrace the fate
Of that dark hour. Resolve yourselves apart;
I'll come to you anon.

BOTH MURDERERS

We are resolved, my lord.

MACBETH

I'll call upon you straight. Abide within.

Exeunt MURDERERS.

It is concluded: Banquo, thy soul's flight,
If it find heaven, must find it out tonight.

Exit.

SCENE II

The palace.

Enter LADY MACBETH *and a* SERVANT.

LADY MACBETH
Is Banquo gone from court?

SERVANT
Ay, madam, but returns again tonight.

LADY MACBETH
Say to the King I would attend his leisure
For a few words.

SERVANT
Madam, I will. [Exit.]

LADY MACBETH
Nought's had, all's spent,
Where our desire is got without content.
'Tis safer to be that which we destroy
Than by destruction dwell in doubtful joy.

Enter MACBETH.

How now, my lord? Why do you keep alone,
Of sorriest fancies your companions making,
Using those thoughts which should indeed
    have died
With them they think on? Things without all
    remedy
Should be without regard. What's done is done.

MACBETH
We have scotch'd the snake, not kill'd it.
She'll close and be herself, whilst our poor malice
Remains in danger of her former tooth.
But let the frame of things disjoint, both the
    worlds suffer,
Ere we will eat our meal in fear and sleep
In the affliction of these terrible dreams
That shake us nightly. Better be with the dead,

Whom we, to gain our peace, have sent to peace,
Than on the torture of the mind to lie
In restless ecstasy. Duncan is in his grave;
After life's fitful fever he sleeps well.
Treason has done his worst; nor steel, nor poison,
Malice domestic, foreign levy, nothing,
Can touch him further.

LADY MACBETH
Come on,
Gentle my lord, sleek o'er your rugged looks;
Be bright and jovial among your guests tonight.

MACBETH
So shall I, love, and so, I pray, be you.
Let your remembrance apply to Banquo;
Present him eminence, both with eye and tongue:
Unsafe the while, that we
Must lave our honours in these flattering streams,
And make our faces vizards to our hearts,
Disguising what they are.

LADY MACBETH
You must leave this.

MACBETH
O, full of scorpions is my mind, dear wife!
Thou know'st that Banquo and his Fleance lives.

LADY MACBETH
But in them nature's copy's not eterne.

MACBETH
There's comfort yet; they are assailable.
Then be thou jocund. Ere the bat hath flown
His cloister'd flight, ere to black Hecate's summons
The shard-borne beetle with his drowsy hums
Hath rung night's yawning peal, there shall be done
A deed of dreadful note.

LADY MACBETH
    What's to be done?

MACBETH
    Be innocent of the knowledge, dearest chuck,
    Till thou applaud the deed. Come, seeling night,
    Scarf up the tender eye of pitiful day,
    And with thy bloody and invisible hand
    Cancel and tear to pieces that great bond
    Which keeps me pale! Light thickens, and the
        crow
    Makes wing to the rooky wood;
    Good things of day begin to droop and drowse,
    Whiles night's black agents to their preys do rouse.
    Thou marvel'st at my words, but hold thee still:
    Things bad begun make strong themselves by ill.
    So, prithee, go with me.

Exeunt.

SCENE III

A park near the palace.

Enter three MURDERERS.

FIRST MURDERER
    But who did bid thee join with us?

THIRD MURDERER
    Macbeth.

SECOND MURDERER
    He needs not our mistrust, since he delivers
    Our offices and what we have to do
    To the direction just.

FIRST MURDERER
Then stand with us.
The west yet glimmers with some streaks of day;
Now spurs the lated traveller apace
To gain the timely inn, and near approaches
The subject of our watch.

THIRD MURDERER
Hark! I hear horses.

BANQUO
[*Within.*] Give us a light there, ho!

SECOND MURDERER
Then 'tis he; the rest
That are within the note of expectation
Already are i' the court.

FIRST MURDERER
His horses go about.

THIRD MURDERER
Almost a mile, but he does usually –
So all men do – from hence to the palace gate
Make it their walk.

SECOND MURDERER
A light, a light!

Enter BANQUO, *and* FLEANCE *with a torch.*

THIRD MURDERER
'Tis he.

FIRST MURDERER
Stand to't.

BANQUO
It will be rain tonight.

FIRST MURDERER
　Let it come down.

They set upon Banquo.

BANQUO
　O, treachery! Fly, good Fleance, fly, fly, fly!
　Thou mayst revenge. O slave! Dies. Fleance escapes.

THIRD MURDERER
　Who did strike out the light?

FIRST MURDERER
　Wast not the way?

THIRD MURDERER
　There's but one down; the son is fled.

SECOND MURDERER
　We have lost
　Best half of our affair.

FIRST MURDERER
　Well, let's away and say how much is done.

Exeunt.

SCENE IV

A Hall in the palace. A banquet prepared.

Enter MACBETH, LADY MACBETH, ROSS, LENNOX, *and* ATTENDANTS.

MACBETH
    You know your own degrees; sit down. At first
    And last the hearty welcome.

LORDS
    Thanks to your Majesty.

MACBETH
    Ourself will mingle with society
    And play the humble host.
    Our hostess keeps her state, but in best time
    We will require her welcome.

LADY MACBETH
    Pronounce it for me, sir, to all our friends,
    For my heart speaks they are welcome.

Enter FIRST MURDERER.

MACBETH
    See, they encounter thee with their hearts' thanks.
    Both sides are even; here I'll sit i' the midst.
    Be large in mirth; anon we'll drink a measure
    The table round. [*Approaches the door.*] There's
       blood upon thy face.

MURDERER
    'Tis Banquo's then.

MACBETH
    'Tis better thee without than he within.
    Is he dispatch'd?

MURDERER
    My lord, his throat is cut; that I did for him.

MACBETH
    Thou art the best o' the cut-throats! Yet he's good
    That did the like for Fleance. If thou didst it,
    Thou art the nonpareil.

MURDERER
    Most royal sir,
    Fleance is 'scaped.

MACBETH
    [*Aside.*] Then comes my fit again. I had else been perfect,
    Whole as the marble, founded as the rock,
    As broad and general as the casing air;
    But now I am cabin'd, cribb'd, confin'd, bound in
    To saucy doubts and fears – But Banquo's safe?

MURDERER
    Ay, my good lord. Safe in a ditch he bides,
    With twenty trenched gashes on his head,
    The least a death to nature.

MACBETH
    Thanks for that.
    There the grown serpent lies; the worm that's fled
    Hath nature that in time will venom breed,
    No teeth for the present. Get thee gone. Tomorrow
    We'll hear ourselves again.

Exit MURDERER.

LADY MACBETH
    My royal lord,
    You do not give the cheer. The feast is sold
    That is not often vouch'd, while 'tis a-making,
    'Tis given with welcome. To feed were best at home;
    From thence the sauce to meat is ceremony;
    Meeting were bare without it.

72

MACBETH

Sweet remembrancer!
Now good digestion wait on appetite,
And health on both!

LENNOX

May't please your Highness sit.

The GHOST OF BANQUO *enters and sits in Macbeth's place.*

MACBETH

Here had we now our country's honour roof'd,
Were the graced person of our Banquo present,
Who may I rather challenge for unkindness
Than pity for mischance!

ROSS

His absence, sir,
Lays blame upon his promise. Please't your Highness
To grace us with your royal company?

MACBETH

The table's full.

LENNOX

Here is a place reserved, sir.

MACBETH

Where?

LENNOX

Here, my good lord. What is't that moves your Highness?

MACBETH

Which of you have done this?

LORDS

What, my good lord?

MACBETH

Thou canst not say I did it; never shake
Thy gory locks at me.

ROSS

Gentlemen, rise; his Highness is well.

LADY MACBETH

Sit, worthy friends; my lord is often thus,
And hath been from his youth. Pray you, keep seat.
The fit is momentary; upon a thought
He will again be well. If much you note him,
You shall offend him and extend his passion.
Feed, and regard him not – Are you a man?

MACBETH

Ay, and a bold one, that dare look on that
Which might appal the devil.

LADY MACBETH

O proper stuff!
This is the very painting of your fear;
This is the air-drawn dagger which you said
Led you to Duncan. O, these flaws and starts,
Impostors to true fear, would well become
A woman's story at a winter's fire,
Authorized by her grandam. Shame itself!
Why do you make such faces? When all's done,
You look but on a stool.

MACBETH

Prithee, see there! Behold! Look! Lo! How say you?
Why, what care I? If thou canst nod, speak too.
If charnel houses and our graves must send
Those that we bury back, our monuments
Shall be the maws of kites.

Exit GHOST.

LADY MACBETH

What, quite unmann'd in folly?

MACBETH

If I stand here, I saw him.

LADY MACBETH

Fie, for shame!

MACBETH

Blood hath been shed ere now, i' the olden time,
Ere humane statute purged the gentle weal;
Ay, and since too, murders have been perform'd
Too terrible for the ear. The time has been,
That, when the brains were out, the man would die,
And there an end; but now they rise again,
With twenty mortal murders on their crowns,
And push us from our stools. This is more strange
Than such a murder is.

LADY MACBETH

My worthy lord,
Your noble friends do lack you.

MACBETH

I do forget.
Do not muse at me, my most worthy friends.
I have a strange infirmity, which is nothing
To those that know me. Come, love and health to all;
Then I'll sit down. Give me some wine, fill full.
I drink to the general joy o' the whole table,
And to our dear friend Banquo, whom we miss.
Would he were here! To all and him we thirst,
And all to all.

LORDS

Our duties and the pledge.

Re-enter GHOST.

MACBETH

Avaunt, and quit my sight! Let the earth hide thee!
Thy bones are marrowless, thy blood is cold;
Thou hast no speculation in those eyes
Which thou dost glare with.

LADY MACBETH

Think of this, good peers,
But as a thing of custom. 'Tis no other,
Only it spoils the pleasure of the time.

MACBETH

What man dare, I dare.
Approach thou like the rugged Russian bear,
The arm'd rhinoceros, or the Hyrcan tiger;
Take any shape but that, and my firm nerves
Shall never tremble. Or be alive again,
And dare me to the desert with thy sword.
If trembling I inhabit then, protest me
The baby of a girl. Hence, horrible shadow!
Unreal mockery, hence!

Exit GHOST.

Why, so, being gone,
I am a man again. Pray you sit still.

LADY MACBETH

You have displaced the mirth, broke the good
    meeting,
With most admired disorder.

MACBETH

Can such things be,
And overcome us like a summer's cloud,
Without our special wonder? You make me strange
Even to the disposition that I owe
When now I think you can behold such sights

And keep the natural ruby of your cheeks
When mine is blanch'd with fear.

ROSS

What sights, my lord?

LADY MACBETH

I pray you, speak not; he grows worse and worse;
Question enrages him. At once, good night.
Stand not upon the order of your going,
But go at once.

LENNOX

Good night, and better health
Attend his Majesty!

LADY MACBETH

A kind good night to all!

Exeunt all but MACBETH *and* LADY MACBETH.

MACBETH

It will have blood; they say blood will have blood.
Stones have been known to move and trees to speak;
Augures and understood relations have
By maggot pies and choughs and rooks brought forth
The secret'st man of blood. What is the night?

LADY MACBETH

Almost at odds with morning, which is which.

MACBETH

How say'st thou, that Macduff denies his person
At our great bidding?

LADY MACBETH

Did you send to him, sir?

MACBETH

I hear it by the way, but I will send.
There's not a one of them but in his house
I keep a servant feed. I will tomorrow,
And betimes I will, to the weird sisters.
More shall they speak; for now I am bent to know,
By the worst means, the worst. For mine own good
All causes shall give way. I am in blood
Stepp'd in so far that, should I wade no more,
Returning were as tedious as go o'er.
Strange things I have in head that will to hand,
Which must be acted ere they may be scann'd.

LADY MACBETH

You lack the season of all natures, sleep.

MACBETH

Come, we'll to sleep. My strange and self-abuse
Is the initiate fear that wants hard use.
We are yet but young in deed.

Exeunt.

SCENE V

A heath. Thunder.

Enter the three WITCHES, *meeting* HECATE.

FIRST WITCH

Why, how now, Hecate? You look angerly.

HECATE

Have I not reason, beldams as you are,
Saucy and overbold? How did you dare
To trade and traffic with Macbeth

In riddles and affairs of death,
And I, the mistress of your charms,
The close contriver of all harms,
Was never call'd to bear my part,
Or show the glory of our art?
And, which is worse, all you have done
Hath been but for a wayward son,
Spiteful and wrathful, who, as others do,
Loves for his own ends, not for you.
But make amends now. Get you gone,
And at the pit of Acheron
Meet me i' the morning. Thither he
Will come to know his destiny.
Your vessels and your spells provide,
Your charms and everything beside.
I am for the air; this night I'll spend
Unto a dismal and a fatal end.
Great business must be wrought ere noon:
Upon the corner of the moon
There hangs a vaporous drop profound;
I'll catch it ere it come to ground.
And that distill'd by magic sleights
Shall raise such artificial sprites
As by the strength of their illusion
Shall draw him on to his confusion.
He shall spurn fate, scorn death, and bear
His hopes 'bove wisdom, grace, and fear.
And you all know security
Is mortals' chiefest enemy.
Music and a song within,
"Come away, come away."
Hark! I am call'd; my little spirit, see,
Sits in a foggy cloud and stays for me.

Exit.

FIRST WITCH
    Come, let's make haste; she'll soon be back again.

Exeunt.

SCENE VI

Forres. The palace.

Enter LENNOX *and another* LORD.

LENNOX
    My former speeches have but hit your thoughts,
    Which can interpret further; only I say
    Thing's have been strangely borne. The gracious
    Duncan
    Was pitied of Macbeth; marry, he was dead.
    And the right valiant Banquo walk'd too late,
    Whom, you may say, if't please you, Fleance kill'd,
    For Fleance fled. Men must not walk too late.
    Who cannot want the thought, how monstrous
    It was for Malcolm and for Donalbain
    To kill their gracious father? Damned fact!
    How it did grieve Macbeth! Did he not straight,
    In pious rage, the two delinquents tear
    That were the slaves of drink and thralls of sleep?
    Was not that nobly done? Ay, and wisely too,
    For 'twould have anger'd any heart alive
    To hear the men deny't. So that, I say,
    He has borne all things well; and I do think
    That, had he Duncan's sons under his key –
    As, an't please heaven, he shall not – they should find
    What 'twere to kill a father; so should Fleance.

But, peace! For from broad words, and 'cause he fail'd
His presence at the tyrant's feast, I hear,
Macduff lives in disgrace. Sir, can you tell
Where he bestows himself?

LORD

The son of Duncan,
From whom this tyrant holds the due of birth,
Lives in the English court and is received
Of the most pious Edward with such grace
That the malevolence of fortune nothing
Takes from his high respect. Thither Macduff
Is gone to pray the holy King, upon his aid
To wake Northumberland and warlike Siward;
That by the help of these, with Him above
To ratify the work, we may again
Give to our tables meat, sleep to our nights,
Free from our feasts and banquets bloody knives,
Do faithful homage, and receive free honours –
All which we pine for now. And this report
Hath so exasperate the King that he
Prepares for some attempt of war.

LENNOX

Sent he to Macduff?

LORD

He did, and with an absolute "Sir, not I,"
The cloudy messenger turns me his back,
And hums, as who should say, "You'll rue the time
That clogs me with this answer."

LENNOX

And that well might
Advise him to a caution, to hold what distance
His wisdom can provide. Some holy angel
Fly to the court of England and unfold
His message ere he come, that a swift blessing

May soon return to this our suffering country
Under a hand accursed!

LORD
I'll send my prayers with him.

Exeunt.

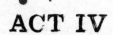

ACT IV

SCENE I

A cavern. In the middle, a boiling cauldron. Thunder.

Enter the three WITCHES.

FIRST WITCH
  Thrice the brinded cat hath mew'd.

SECOND WITCH
  Thrice and once the hedge-pig whined.

THIRD WITCH
  Harpier cries, "'Tis time, 'tis time."

FIRST WITCH
  Round about the cauldron go;
  In the poison'd entrails throw.
  Toad, that under cold stone
  Days and nights has thirty-one
  Swelter'd venom sleeping got,
  Boil thou first i' the charmed pot.

ALL
  Double, double, toil and trouble;
  Fire burn and cauldron bubble.

SECOND WITCH
  Fillet of a fenny snake,
  In the cauldron boil and bake;
  Eye of newt and toe of frog,

83

Wool of bat and tongue of dog,
Adder's fork and blind-worm's sting,
Lizard's leg and howlet's wing,
For a charm of powerful trouble,
Like a hell-broth boil and bubble.

ALL
Double, double, toil and trouble;
Fire burn and cauldron bubble.

THIRD WITCH
Scale of dragon, tooth of wolf,
Witch's mummy, maw and gulf
Of the ravin'd salt-sea shark,
Root of hemlock digg'd i' the dark,
Liver of blaspheming Jew,
Gall of goat and slips of yew
Sliver'd in the moon's eclipse,
Nose of Turk and Tartar's lips,
Finger of birth-strangled babe
Ditch-deliver'd by a drab,
Make the gruel thick and slab.
Add thereto a tiger's chawdron,
For the ingredients of our cawdron.

ALL
Double, double, toil and trouble;
Fire burn and cauldron bubble.

SECOND WITCH
Cool it with a baboon's blood,
Then the charm is firm and good.

Enter HECATE.

HECATE
O, well done! I commend your pains,
And everyone shall share i' the gains.

And now about the cauldron sing,
Like elves and fairies in a ring,
Enchanting all that you put in.

Music and a song, "Black spirits". HECATE *retires.*

SECOND WITCH
By the pricking of my thumbs,
Something wicked this way comes.
Open, locks,
Whoever knocks!

Enter MACBETH.

MACBETH
How now, you secret, black, and midnight hags?
What is't you do?

ALL
A deed without a name.

MACBETH
I conjure you, by that which you profess
(Howe'er you come to know it) answer me:
Though you untie the winds and let them fight
Against the churches, though the yesty waves
Confound and swallow navigation up,
Though bladed corn be lodged and trees blown down,
Though castles topple on their warders' heads,
Though palaces and pyramids do slope
Their heads to their foundations, though the treasure
Of nature's germaines tumble all together
Even till destruction sicken, answer me
To what I ask you.

FIRST WITCH
Speak.

SECOND WITCH
Demand.

THIRD WITCH
We'll answer.

FIRST WITCH
Say, if thou'dst rather hear it from our mouths,
Or from our masters'?

MACBETH
Call 'em, let me see 'em.

FIRST WITCH
Pour in sow's blood that hath eaten
Her nine farrow; grease that's sweaten
From the murderer's gibbet throw
Into the flame.

ALL
Come, high or low;
Thyself and office deftly show!

Thunder. FIRST APPARITION: *an armed Head.*

MACBETH
Tell me, thou unknown power –

FIRST WITCH
He knows thy thought:
Hear his speech, but say thou nought.

FIRST APPARITION
Macbeth! Macbeth! Macbeth! Beware Macduff,
Beware the Thane of Fife. Dismiss me. Enough. [*Descends.*]

MACBETH
Whate'er thou art, for thy good caution, thanks;
Thou hast harp'd my fear aright. But one word more –

FIRST WITCH
He will not be commanded. Here's another,
More potent than the first.

Thunder. SECOND APPARITION: *a bloody Child.*

SECOND APPARITION
Macbeth! Macbeth! Macbeth!

MACBETH
Had I three ears, I'd hear thee.

SECOND APPARITION
Be bloody, bold, and resolute: laugh to scorn
The power of man, for none of woman born
Shall harm Macbeth. [*Descends.*]

MACBETH
Then live, Macduff. What need I fear of thee?
But yet I'll make assurance double sure,
And take a bond of fate: thou shalt not live,
That I may tell pale-hearted fear it lies,
And sleep in spite of thunder.

Thunder. THIRD APPARITION: *a Child crowned,
with a tree in his hand.*

What is this,
That rises like the issue of a king,
And wears upon his baby brow the round
And top of sovereignty?

ALL
Listen, but speak not to't.

THIRD APPARITION
Be lion-mettled, proud, and take no care
Who chafes, who frets, or where conspirers are.
Macbeth shall never vanquish'd be until
Great Birnam Wood to high Dunsinane Hill
Shall come against him. [*Descends.*]

MACBETH
That will never be.
Who can impress the forest, bid the tree
Unfix his earth-bound root? Sweet bodements, good!
Rebellion's head, rise never till the Wood
Of Birnam rise, and our high-placed Macbeth
Shall live the lease of nature, pay his breath
To time and mortal custom. Yet my heart
Throbs to know one thing: tell me, if your art
Can tell so much, shall Banquo's issue ever
Reign in this kingdom?

ALL
Seek to know no more.

MACBETH
I will be satisfied! Deny me this,
And an eternal curse fall on you! Let me know.
Why sinks that cauldron, and what noise is this?

Hautboys.

FIRST WITCH
Show!

SECOND WITCH
Show!

THIRD. WITCH
Show!

ALL
    Show his eyes, and grieve his heart;
    Come like shadows, so depart!

A show of EIGHT KINGS, *the last with a glass in his hand;*
BANQUO'S GHOST *following.*

MACBETH
    Thou are too like the spirit of Banquo Down!
    Thy crown does sear mine eyeballs. And thy hair,
    Thou other gold-bound brow, is like the first.
    A third is like the former. Filthy hags!
    Why do you show me this? A fourth! Start, eyes!
    What, will the line stretch out to the crack of doom?
    Another yet! A seventh! I'll see no more!
    And yet the eighth appears, who bears a glass
    Which shows me many more; and some I see
    That twofold balls and treble sceptres carry.
    Horrible sight! Now I see 'tis true;
    For the blood-bolter'd Banquo smiles upon me,
    And points at them for his. What, is this so?

FIRST WITCH
    Ay, sir, all this is so. But why
    Stands Macbeth thus amazedly?
    Come, sisters, cheer we up his sprites,
    And show the best of our delights.
    I'll charm the air to give a sound,
    While you perform your antic round,
    That this great King may kindly say
    Our duties did his welcome pay.

Music. The WITCHES *dance and then vanish*
with HECATE.

MACBETH
Where are they? Gone? Let this pernicious hour
Stand ay accursed in the calendar!
Come in, without there!

Enter LENNOX.

LENNOX
What's your Grace's will?

MACBETH
Saw you the weird sisters?

LENNOX
No, my lord.

MACBETH
Came they not by you?

LENNOX
No indeed, my lord.

MACBETH
Infected be the 'air whereon they ride,
And damn'd all those that trust them! I did hear
The galloping of horse. Who wast came by?

LENNOX
'Tis two or three, my lord, that bring you word
Macduff is fled to England.

MACBETH
Fled to England?

LENNOX
Ay, my good lord.

MACBETH
[*Aside.*] Time, thou anticipatest my dread exploits.
The flighty purpose never is o'ertook

Unless the deed go with it. From this moment
The very firstlings of my heart shall be
The firstlings of my hand. And even now,
To crown my thoughts with acts, be it thought
and done:
The castle of Macduff I will surprise,
Seize upon Fife, give to the edge o' the sword
His wife, his babes, and all unfortunate souls
That trace him in his line. No boasting like a fool;
This deed I'll do before this purpose cool.
But no more sights! – Where are these gentlemen?
Come, bring me where they are.

Exeunt.

SCENE II

Fife. Macduff's castle.

Enter LADY MACDUFF, HER SON, *and* ROSS.

LADY MACDUFF
    What had he done, to make him fly the land?

ROSS
    You must have patience, madam.

LADY MACDUFF
    He had none;
    His flight was madness. When our actions do not,
    Our fears do make us traitors.

ROSS
    You know not
    Whether it was his wisdom or his fear.

LADY MACDUFF

Wisdom? To leave his wife, to leave his babes,
His mansion, and his titles, in a place
From whence himself does fly? He loves us not;
He wants the natural touch; for the poor wren,
The most diminutive of birds, will fight,
Her young ones in her nest, against the owl.
All is the fear and nothing is the love;
As little is the wisdom, where the flight
So runs against all reason.

ROSS

My dearest coz,
I pray you, school yourself. But for your husband,
He is noble, wise, judicious, and best knows
The fits o' the season. I dare not speak much further;
But cruel are the times when we are traitors
And do not know ourselves; when we hold rumour
From what we fear, yet know not what we fear,
But float upon a wild and violent sea
Each way and move. I take my leave of you;
Shall not be long but I'll be here again.
Things at the worst will cease or else climb upward
To what they were before. My pretty cousin,
Blessing upon you!

LADY MACDUFF

Father'd he is, and yet he's fatherless.

ROSS

I am so much a fool, should I stay longer,
It would be my disgrace and your discomfort.
I take my leave at once. [*Exit.*]

LADY MACDUFF

Sirrah, your father's dead.
And what will you do now? How will you live?

SON

As birds do, Mother.

LADY MACDUFF

What, with worms and flies?

SON

With what I get, I mean; and so do they.

LADY MACDUFF

Poor bird! Thou'dst never fear the net nor lime,
The pitfall nor the gin.

SON

Why should I, Mother? Poor birds they are not set for.
My father is not dead, for all your saying.

LADY MACDUFF

Yes, he is dead. How wilt thou do for father?

SON

Nay, how will you do for a husband?

LADY MACDUFF

Why, I can buy me twenty at any market.

SON

Then you'll buy 'em to sell again.

LADY MACDUFF

Thou speak'st with all thy wit, and yet, i' faith,
With wit enough for thee.

SON

Was my father a traitor, Mother?

LADY MACDUFF

Ay, that he was.

SON

What is a traitor?

LADY MACDUFF
Why one that swears and lies.

SON
And be all traitors that do so?

LADY MACDUFF
Everyone that does so is a traitor and must be hanged.

SON
And must they all be hanged that swear and lie?

LADY MACDUFF
Everyone.

SON
Who must hang them?

LADY MACDUFF
Why, the honest men.

SON
Then the liars and swearers are fools, for there are liars and swearers enow to beat the honest men and hang up them.

LADY MACDUFF
Now, God help thee, poor monkey! But how wilt thou do for a father?

SON
If he were dead, you'd weep for him; if you would not, it were a good sign that I should quickly have a new father.

LADY MACDUFF
Poor prattler, how thou talk'st!

Enter a MESSENGER.

MESSENGER

Bless you, fair dame! I am not to you known,
Though in your state of honour I am perfect.
I doubt some danger does approach you nearly.
If you will take a homely man's advice,
Be not found here; hence, with your little ones.
To fright you thus, methinks I am too savage;
To do worse to you were fell cruelty,
Which is too nigh your person. Heaven preserve you!
I dare abide no longer. [*Exit.*]

LADY MACDUFF

Whither should I fly?
I have done no harm. But I remember now
I am in this earthly world, where to do harm
Is often laudable, to do good sometime
Accounted dangerous folly. Why then, alas,
Do I put up that womanly defence,
To say I have done no harm – What are these faces?

Enter MURDERERS.

FIRST MURDERER

Where is your husband?

LADY MACDUFF

I hope, in no place so unsanctified
Where such as thou mayst find him.

FIRST MURDERER

He's a traitor.

SON

Thou liest, thou shag-ear'd villain!

FIRST MURDERER

What, you egg!

Stabs him.

Young fry of treachery!

SON
Now, Mother.

He has kill'd me, Mother.
Run away, I pray you! [*Dies.*]

Exit LADY MACDUFF, *crying* "Murder!"

Exeunt MURDERERS, *following her.*

SCENE III

England. Before the King's palace.

Enter MALCOLM *and* MACDUFF.

MALCOLM
Let us seek out some desolate shade and there
Weep our sad bosoms empty.

MACDUFF
Let us rather
Hold fast the mortal sword, and like good men
Bestride our downfall'n birthdom. Each new morn
New widows howl, new orphans cry, new sorrows
Strike heaven on the face, that it resounds
As if it felt with Scotland and yell'd out
Like syllable of dolour.

MALCOLM
What I believe, I'll wail;
What know, believe; and what I can redress,
As I shall find the time to friend, I will.

What you have spoke, it may be so perchance.
This tyrant, whose sole name blisters our tongues,
Was once thought honest. You have loved him well;
He hath not touch'd you yet. I am young, but something
You may deserve of him through me, and wisdom
To offer up a weak, poor, innocent lamb
To appease an angry god.

MACDUFF

I am not treacherous.

MALCOLM

But Macbeth is.
A good and virtuous nature may recoil
In an imperial charge. But I shall crave your pardon;
That which you are, my thoughts cannot transpose.
Angels are bright still, though the brightest fell.
Though all things foul would wear the brows of grace,
Yet grace must still look so.

MACDUFF

I have lost my hopes.

MALCOLM

Perchance even there where I did find my doubts.
Why in that rawness left you wife and child,
Those precious motives, those strong knots of love,
Without leave-taking? I pray you,
Let not my jealousies be your dishonours,
But mine own safeties. You may be rightly just,
Whatever I shall think.

MACDUFF

Bleed, bleed, poor country!
Great tyranny, lay thou thy basis sure,
For goodness dare not check thee. Wear thou thy wrongs;
The title is affeer'd. Fare thee well, lord.
I would not be the villain that thou think'st

For the whole space that's in the tyrant's grasp
And the rich East to boot.

MALCOLM
Be not offended;
I speak not as in absolute fear of you.
I think our country sinks beneath the yoke;
It weeps, it bleeds, and each new day a gash
Is added to her wounds. I think withal
There would be hands uplifted in my right;
And here from gracious England have I offer
Of goodly thousands. But for all this,
When I shall tread upon the tyrant's head,
Or wear it on my sword, yet my poor country
Shall have more vices than it had before,
More suffer and more sundry ways than ever,
By him that shall succeed.

MACDUFF
What should he be?

MALCOLM
It is myself I mean, in whom I know
All the particulars of vice so grafted
That, when they shall be open'd, black Macbeth
Will seem as pure as snow, and the poor state
Esteem him as a lamb, being compared
With my confineless harms.

MACDUFF
Not in the legions
Of horrid hell can come a devil more damn'd
In evils to top Macbeth.

MALCOLM
I grant him bloody,
Luxurious, avaricious, false, deceitful,
Sudden, malicious, smacking of every sin

That has a name. But there's no bottom, none,
In my voluptuousness. Your wives, your daughters,
Your matrons, and your maids could not fill up
The cistern of my lust, and my desire
All continent impediments would o'erbear
That did oppose my will. Better Macbeth
Than such an one to reign.

MACDUFF
Boundless intemperance
In nature is a tyranny; it hath been
The untimely emptying of the happy throne,
And fall of many kings. But fear not yet
To take upon you what is yours. You may
Convey your pleasures in a spacious plenty
And yet seem cold, the time you may so hoodwink.
We have willing dames enough; there cannot be
That vulture in you to devour so many
As will to greatness dedicate themselves,
Finding it so inclined.

MALCOLM
With this there grows
In my most ill-composed affection such
A stanchless avarice that, were I King,
I should cut off the nobles for their lands,
Desire his jewels and this other's house,
And my more-having would be as a sauce
To make me hunger more, that I should forge
Quarrels unjust against the good and loyal,
Destroying them for wealth.

MACDUFF
This avarice
Sticks deeper, grows with more pernicious root
Than summer-seeming lust, and it hath been
The sword of our slain kings. Yet do not fear;

Scotland hath foisons to fill up your will
Of your mere own. All these are portable,
With other graces weigh'd.

MALCOLM
But I have none. The king-becoming graces,
As justice, verity, temperance, stableness,
Bounty, perseverance, mercy, lowliness,
Devotion, patience, courage, fortitude,
I have no relish of them, but abound
In the division of each several crime,
Acting it many ways. Nay, had I power, I should
Pour the sweet milk of concord into hell,
Uproar the universal peace, confound
All unity on earth.

MACDUFF
O Scotland, Scotland!

MALCOLM
If such a one be fit to govern, speak.
I am as I have spoken.

MACDUFF
Fit to govern?
No, not to live. O nation miserable!
With an untitled tyrant bloody-scepter'd,
When shalt thou see thy wholesome days again,
Since that the truest issue of thy throne
By his own interdiction stands accursed
And does blaspheme his breed? Thy royal father
Was a most sainted king; the queen that bore thee,
Oftener upon her knees than on her feet,
Died every day she lived. Fare thee well!
These evils thou repeat'st upon thyself
Have banish'd me from Scotland. O my breast,
Thy hope ends here!

MALCOLM

    Macduff, this noble passion,
    Child of integrity, hath from my soul
    Wiped the black scruples, reconciled my
       thoughts
    To thy good truth and honour. Devilish Macbeth
    By many of these trains hath sought to win me
    Into his power, and modest wisdom plucks me
    From over-credulous haste. But God above
    Deal between thee and me! For even now
    I put myself to thy direction and
    Unspeak mine own detraction; here abjure
    The taints and blames I laid upon myself,
    For strangers to my nature. I am yet
    Unknown to woman, never was forsworn,
    Scarcely have coveted what was mine own,
    At no time broke my faith, would not betray
    The devil to his fellow, and delight
    No less in truth than life. My first false speaking
    Was this upon myself. What I am truly
    Is thine and my poor country's to command.
    Whither indeed, before thy here – approach,
    Old Siward, with ten thousand warlike men
    Already at a point, was setting forth.
    Now we'll together, and the chance of goodness
    Be like our warranted quarrel! Why are you silent?

MACDUFF

    Such welcome and unwelcome things at once
    'Tis hard to reconcile.

Enter a DOCTOR.

MALCOLM

    Well, more anon. Comes the King forth, I pray you?

DOCTOR

Ay, sir, there are a crew of wretched souls
That stay his cure. Their malady convinces
The great assay of art, but at his touch,
Such sanctity hath heaven given his hand,
They presently amend.

MALCOLM

I thank you, Doctor.

Exit DOCTOR.

MACDUFF

What's the disease he means?

MALCOLM

'Tis call'd the evil:
A most miraculous work in this good King,
Which often, since my here-remain in England,
I have seen him do. How he solicits heaven,
Himself best knows; but strangely-visited people,
All swoll'n and ulcerous, pitiful to the eye,
The mere despair of surgery, he cures,
Hanging a golden stamp about their necks
Put on with holy prayers; and 'tis spoken,
To the succeeding royalty he leaves
The healing benediction. With this strange virtue
He hath a heavenly gift of prophecy,
And sundry blessings hang about his throne
That speak him full of grace.

Enter ROSS.

MACDUFF

See, who comes here?

MALCOLM

My countryman, but yet I know him not.

MACDUFF

My ever gentle cousin, welcome hither.

MALCOLM

I know him now. Good God, betimes remove
The means that makes us strangers!

ROSS

Sir, amen.

MACDUFF

Stands Scotland where it did?

ROSS

Alas, poor country,
Almost afraid to know itself! It cannot
Be call'd our mother, but our grave. Where nothing,
But who knows nothing, is once seen to smile;
Where sighs and groans and shrieks that rend
    the air,
Are made, not mark'd; where violent sorrow seems
A modern ecstasy. The dead man's knell
Is there scarce ask'd for who, and good men's lives
Expire before the flowers in their caps,
Dying or ere they sicken.

MACDUFF

O, relation
Too nice, and yet too true!

MALCOLM

What's the newest grief?

ROSS

That of an hour's age doth hiss the speaker;
Each minute teems a new one.

MACDUFF

How does my wife?

ROSS

Why, well.

MACDUFF

And all my children?

ROSS

Well too.

MACDUFF

The tyrant has not batter'd at their peace?

ROSS

No, they were well at peace when I did leave 'em.

MACDUFF

Be not a niggard of your speech. How goest?

ROSS

When I came hither to transport the tidings,
Which I have heavily borne, there ran a rumour
Of many worthy fellows that were out,
Which was to my belief witness'd the rather,
For that I saw the tyrant's power afoot.
Now is the time of help; your eye in Scotland
Would create soldiers, make our women fight,
To doff their dire distresses.

MALCOLM

Be't their comfort
We are coming thither. Gracious England hath
Lent us good Siward and ten thousand men;
An older and a better soldier none
That Christendom gives out.

ROSS
    Would I could answer
    This comfort with the like! But I have words
    That would be howl'd out in the desert air,
    Where hearing should not latch them.

MACDUFF
    What concern they?
    The general cause? Or is it a fee-grief
    Due to some single breast?

ROSS
    No mind that's honest
    But in it shares some woe, though the main part
    Pertains to you alone.

MACDUFF
    If it be mine,
    Keep it not from me, quickly let me have it.

ROSS
    Let not your ears despise my tongue forever,
    Which shall possess them with the heaviest sound
    That ever yet they heard.

MACDUFF
    Humh! I guess at it.

ROSS
    Your castle is surprised; your wife and babes
    Savagely slaughter'd. To relate the manner
    Were, on the quarry of these murder'd deer,
    To add the death of you.

MALCOLM
    Merciful heaven!
    What, man! Ne'er pull your hat upon your brows;
    Give sorrow words. The grief that does not speak
    Whispers the o'erfraught heart, and bids it break.

MACDUFF

My children too?

ROSS

Wife, children, servants, all
That could be found.

MACDUFF

And I must be from thence!
My wife kill'd too?

ROSS

I have said.

MALCOLM

Be comforted.
Let's make us medicines of our great revenge,
To cure this deadly grief.

MACDUFF

He has no children. All my pretty ones?
Did you say all? O hell-kite! All?
What, all my pretty chickens and their dam
At one fell swoop?

MALCOLM

Dispute it like a man.

MACDUFF

I shall do so,
But I must also feel it as a man.
I cannot but remember such things were
That were most precious to me. Did heaven
    look on,
And would not take their part? Sinful Macduff,
They were all struck for thee! Naught that I am,
Not for their own demerits, but for mine,
Fell slaughter on their souls. Heaven rest
    them now!

MALCOLM

    Be this the whetstone of your sword. Let grief
    Convert to anger; blunt not the heart, enrage it.

MACDUFF

    O, I could play the woman with mine eyes
    And braggart with my tongue! But, gentle heavens,
    Cut short all intermission; front to front
    Bring thou this fiend of Scotland and myself;
    Within my sword's length set him; if he 'scape,
    Heaven forgive him too!

MALCOLM

    This tune goes manly.
    Come, go we to the King; our power is ready,
    Our lack is nothing but our leave. Macbeth
    Is ripe for shaking, and the powers above
    Put on their instruments. Receive what cheer you may,
    The night is long that never finds the day.

Exeunt.

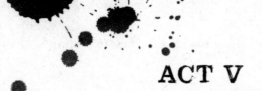

ACT V

SCENE I

Dunsinane. Anteroom in the castle.

Enter a DOCTOR OF PHYSIC *and a* WAITING GENTLEWOMAN.

DOCTOR
I have two nights watched with you, but can perceive no truth in your report. When was it she last walked?

GENTLEWOMAN
Since his Majesty went into the field, have seen her rise from her bed, throw her nightgown upon her, unlock her closet, take forth paper, fold it, write upon't, read it, afterwards seal it, and again return to bed; yet all this while in a most fast sleep.

DOCTOR
A great perturbation in nature, to receive at once the benefit of sleep and do the effects of watching! In this slumbery agitation, besides her walking and other actual performances, what, at any time, have you heard her say?

GENTLEWOMAN
That, sir, which I will not report after her.

DOCTOR
You may to me, and 'tis most meet you should.

GENTLEWOMAN
Neither to you nor anyone, having no witness to confirm my speech.

Enter LADY MACBETH *with a taper.*

Lo you, here she comes! This is her very guise, and, upon my life, fast asleep. Observe her; stand close.

DOCTOR
How came she by that light?

GENTLEWOMAN
Why, it stood by her. She has light by her continually; 'tis her command.

DOCTOR
You see, her eyes are open.

GENTLEWOMAN
Ay, but their sense is shut.

DOCTOR
What is it she does now? Look how she rubs her hands.

GENTLEWOMAN
It is an accustomed action with her, to seem thus washing her hands. I have known her continue in this a quarter of an hour.

LADY MACBETH
Yet here's a spot.

DOCTOR
Hark, she speaks! I will set down what comes from her, to satisfy my remembrance the more strongly.

LADY MACBETH
Out, damned spot! Out, I say! One – two – why then 'tis time to do't. Hell is murky. Fie, my lord, fie! A soldier, and

afeard? What need we fear who knows it, when none can call our power to account? Yet who would have thought the old man to have had so much blood in him?

DOCTOR
Do you mark that?

LADY MACBETH
The Thane of Fife had a wife; where is she now? What, will these hands ne'er be clean? No more o' that, my lord, no more o' that. You mar all with this starting.

DOCTOR
Go to, go to; you have known what you should not.

GENTLEWOMAN
She has spoke what she should not, I am sure of that. Heaven knows what she has known.

LADY MACBETH
Here's the smell of the blood still. All the perfumes of Arabia will not sweeten this little hand. Oh, oh, oh!

DOCTOR
What a sigh is there! The heart is sorely charged.

GENTLEWOMAN
I would not have such a heart in my bosom for the dignity of the whole body.

DOCTOR
Well, well, well –

GENTLEWOMAN
Pray God it be, sir.

DOCTOR
This disease is beyond my practice. Yet I have known those which have walked in their sleep who have died holily in their beds.

LADY MACBETH
    Wash your hands, put on your nightgown, look not so pale.
    I tell you yet again, Banquo's buried; he cannot come out
    on's grave.

DOCTOR
    Even so?

LADY MACBETH
    To bed, to bed; there's knocking at the gate. Come,
    come, come, come, give me your hand. What's done
        cannot be undone.
    To bed, to bed, to bed. [*Exit.*]

DOCTOR
    Will she go now to bed?

GENTLEWOMAN
    Directly.

DOCTOR
    Foul whisperings are abroad. Unnatural deeds
    Do breed unnatural troubles; infected minds
    To their deaf pillows will discharge their secrets.
    More needs she the divine than the physician.
    God, God, forgive us all! Look after her;
    Remove from her the means of all annoyance,
    And still keep eyes upon her. So good night.
    My mind she has mated and amazed my sight.
    I think, but dare not speak.

GENTLEWOMAN
    Good night, good doctor.

Exeunt.

SCENE II

The country near Dunsinane. Drum and colours.

Enter MENTEITH, CAITHNESS, ANGUS, LENNOX, and SOLDIERS.

MENTEITH
    The English power is near, led on by Malcolm,
    His uncle Siward, and the good Macduff.
    Revenges burn in them, for their dear causes
    Would to the bleeding and the grim alarm
    Excite the mortified man.

ANGUS
    Near Birnam Wood
    Shall we well meet them; that way are they coming.

CAITHNESS
    Who knows if Donalbain be with his brother?

LENNOX
    For certain, sir, he is not; I have a file
    Of all the gentry. There is Siward's son
    And many unrough youths that even now
    Protest their first of manhood.

MENTEITH
    What does the tyrant?

CAITHNESS
    Great Dunsinane he strongly fortifies.
    Some say he's mad; others, that lesser hate him,
    Do call it valiant fury; but, for certain,
    He cannot buckle his distemper'd cause
    Within the belt of rule.

ANGUS

Now does he feel
His secret murders sticking on his hands,
Now minutely revolts upbraid his faith-breach;
Those he commands move only in command,
Nothing in love. Now does he feel his title
Hang loose about him, like a giant's robe
Upon a dwarfish thief.

MENTEITH

Who then shall blame
His pester'd senses to recoil and start,
When all that is within him does condemn
Itself for being there?

CAITHNESS

Well, march we on
To give obedience where 'tis truly owed.
Meet we the medicine of the sickly weal,
And with him pour we, in our country's purge,
Each drop of us.

LENNOX

Or so much as it needs
To dew the sovereign flower and drown the weeds.
Make we our march towards Birnam.

Exeunt marching.

SCENE III

Dunsinane. A room in the castle.

Enter MACBETH, DOCTOR, *and* ATTENDANTS.

MACBETH
Bring me no more reports; let them fly all!
Till Birnam Wood remove to Dunsinane
I cannot taint with fear. What's the boy Malcolm?
Was he not born of woman? The spirits that know
All mortal consequences have pronounced me thus:
"Fear not, Macbeth; no man that's born of woman
Shall e'er have power upon thee." Then fly, false
    Thanes,
And mingle with the English epicures!
The mind I sway by and the heart I bear
Shall never sag with doubt nor shake with fear.

Enter a SERVANT.

The devil damn thee black, thou cream-faced loon!
Where got'st thou that goose look?

SERVANT
There is ten thousand –

MACBETH
Geese, villain?

SERVANT
Soldiers, sir.

MACBETH
Go prick thy face and over-red thy fear,
Thou lily-liver'd boy. What soldiers, patch?
Death of thy soul! Those linen cheeks of thine
Are counsellors to fear. What soldiers, whey-face?

SERVANT
The English force, so please you.

MACBETH
Take thy face hence.

Exit Servant.

Seyton – I am sick at heart,
When I behold – Seyton, I say! – This push
Will cheer me ever or disseat me now.
I have lived long enough. My way of life
Is fall'n into the sear, the yellow leaf,
And that which should accompany old age,
As honour, love, obedience, troops of friends,
I must not look to have; but in their stead,
Curses, not loud but deep, mouth-honour, breath,
Which the poor heart would fain deny and
dare not. Seyton!

Enter SEYTON.

SEYTON
What's your gracious pleasure?

MACBETH
What news more?

SEYTON
All is confirm'd, my lord, which was reported.

MACBETH
I'll fight, 'til from my bones my flesh be hack'd.
Give me my armour.

SEYTON
'Tis not needed yet.

MACBETH
I'll put it on.
Send out more horses, skirr the country round,
Hang those that talk of fear. Give me mine armour.
How does your patient, doctor?

DOCTOR
Not so sick, my lord,
As she is troubled with thick-coming fancies,
That keep her from her rest.

MACBETH
Cure her of that.
Canst thou not minister to a mind diseased,
Pluck from the memory a rooted sorrow,
Raze out the written troubles of the brain,
And with some sweet oblivious antidote
Cleanse the stuff'd bosom of that perilous stuff
Which weighs upon the heart?

DOCTOR
Therein the patient
Must minister to himself.

MACBETH
Throw physic to the dogs, I'll none of it.
Come, put mine armour on; give me my staff.
Seyton, send out. Doctor, the Thanes fly from me.
Come, sir, dispatch. If thou couldst, doctor, cast
The water of my land, find her disease
And purge it to a sound and pristine health,
I would applaud thee to the very echo,
That should applaud again. Pull't off, I say.
What rhubarb, cyme, or what purgative drug
Would scour these English hence? Hearst thou of them?

DOCTOR
Ay, my good lord, your royal preparation
Makes us hear something.

MACBETH
Bring it after me.
I will not be afraid of death and bane
Till Birnam Forest come to Dunsinane.

DOCTOR
    [*Aside.*] Were I from Dunsinane away and clear,
    Profit again should hardly draw me here.

Exeunt.

SCENE IV

Country near Birnam Wood. Drum and colours.

Enter MALCOLM, OLD SIWARD *and* HIS SON,
MACDUFF, MENTEITH, CAITHNESS,
ANGUS, LENNOX, ROSS, *and* SOLDIERS, *marching.*

MALCOLM
    Cousins, I hope the days are near at hand
    That chambers will be safe.

MENTEITH
    We doubt it nothing.

SIWARD
    What wood is this before us?

MENTEITH
    The Wood of Birnam.

MALCOLM
    Let every soldier hew him down a bough,
    And bear't before him; thereby shall we shadow
    The numbers of our host, and make discovery
    Err in report of us.

SOLDIERS
    It shall be done.

SIWARD
>We learn no other but the confident tyrant
>Keeps still in Dunsinane and will endure
>Our setting down before't.

MALCOLM
>'Tis his main hope;
>For where there is advantage to be given,
>Both more and less have given him the revolt,
>And none serve with him but constrained things
>Whose hearts are absent too.

MACDUFF
>Let our just censures
>Attend the true event, and put we on
>Industrious soldiership.

SIWARD
>The time approaches
>That will with due decision make us know
>What we shall say we have and what we owe.
>Thoughts speculative their unsure hopes relate,
>But certain issue strokes must arbitrate.
>Towards which advance the war.

Exeunt Marching.

SCENE V

Dunsinane. Within the castle.

Enter MACBETH, SEYTON, and SOLDIERS, with drum and colours.

MACBETH

Hang out our banners on the outward walls;
The cry is still, "They come!" Our castle's strength
Will laugh a siege to scorn. Here let them lie
Till famine and the ague eat them up.
Were they not forced with those that should be ours,
We might have met them dareful, beard to beard,
And beat them backward home.

A cry of women within.

What is that noise?

SEYTON

It is the cry of women, my good lord. [*Exit.*]

MACBETH

I have almost forgot the taste of fears:
The time has been, my senses would have cool'd
To hear a night-shriek, and my fell of hair
Would at a dismal treatise rouse and stir
As life were in't. I have supp'd full with horrors;
Direness, familiar to my slaughterous thoughts,
Cannot once start me.

Re-enter SEYTON.

Wherefore was that cry?

SEYTON

The Queen, my lord, is dead.

MACBETH

She should have died hereafter;
There would have been a time for such a word.
Tomorrow, and tomorrow, and tomorrow
Creeps in this petty pace from day to day
To the last syllable of recorded time;

And all our yesterdays have lighted fools
The way to dusty death. Out, out, brief candle!
Life's but a walking shadow, a poor player
That struts and frets his hour upon the stage
And then is heard no more. It is a tale
Told by an idiot, full of sound and fury,
Signifying nothing.

Enter a MESSENGER.

Thou comest to use thy tongue; thy story quickly.

MESSENGER
Gracious my lord,
I should report that which I say I saw,
But know not how to do it.

MACBETH
Well, say, sir.

MESSENGER
As I did stand my watch upon the hill,
I look'd toward Birnam, and anon, methought,
The Wood began to move.

MACBETH
Liar and slave!

MESSENGER
Let me endure your wrath, if't be not so.
Within this three mile may you see it coming;
I say, a moving grove.

MACBETH
If thou speak'st false,
Upon the next tree shalt thou hang alive,
Till famine cling thee; if thy speech be sooth,
I care not if thou dost for me as much.
I pull in resolution and begin

To doubt the equivocation of the fiend
That lies like truth. "Fear not, till Birnam Wood
Do come to Dunsinane," and now a wood
Comes toward Dunsinane. Arm, arm, and out!
If this which he avouches does appear,
There is nor flying hence nor tarrying here.
I 'gin to be aweary of the sun
And wish the estate o' the world were now undone.
Ring the alarum bell! Blow, wind! Come, wrack!
At least we'll die with harness on our back.

Exeunt.

SCENE VI

Dunsinane. Before the castle.

Enter MALCOLM, OLD SIWARD, MACDUFF, *and their
Army, with boughs.*
Drum and colours.

MALCOLM
    Now near enough; your leafy screens throw down,
    And show like those you are. You, worthy uncle,
    Shall with my cousin, your right noble son,
    Lead our first battle. Worthy Macduff and we
    Shall take upon 's what else remains to do,
    According to our order.

SIWARD
    Fare you well.
    Do we but find the tyrant's power tonight,
    Let us be beaten if we cannot fight.

MACDUFF
    Make all our trumpets speak, give them all breath,
    Those clamorous harbingers of blood and death.

Exeunt.

SCENE VII

Dunsinane. Before the castle. Alarums.

Enter MACBETH.

MACBETH
    They have tied me to a stake; I cannot fly,
    But bear-like I must fight the course. What's he
    That was not born of woman? Such a one
    Am I to fear, or none.

Enter YOUNG SIWARD.

YOUNG SIWARD
    What is thy name?

MACBETH
    Thou'lt be afraid to hear it.

YOUNG SIWARD
    No, though thou call'st thyself a hotter name
    Than any is in hell.

MACBETH
    My name's Macbeth.

YOUNG SIWARD
    The devil himself could not pronounce a title
    More hateful to mine ear.

MACBETH
    No, nor more fearful.

YOUNG SIWARD
    O Thou liest, abhorred tyrant; with my sword
    I'll prove the lie thou speak'st.

They fight, and YOUNG SIWARD *is slain.*

MACBETH
    Thou wast born of woman.
    But swords I smile at, weapons laugh to scorn,
    Brandish'd by man that's of a woman born. [*Exit.*]

Alarums. Enter MACDUFF.

MACDUFF
    That way the noise is. Tyrant, show thy face!
    If thou best slain and with no stroke of mine,
    My wife and children's ghosts will haunt me still.
    I cannot strike at wretched kerns, whose arms
    Are hired to bear their staves. Either thou, Macbeth,
    Or else my sword, with an unbatter'd edge,
    I sheathe again undeeded. There thou shouldst be;
    By this great clatter, one of greatest note
    Seems bruited. Let me find him, Fortune!
    And more I beg not. [*Exit. Alarums.*]

Enter MALCOLM *and* OLD SIWARD.

SIWARD
    This way, my lord; the castle's gently render'd.
    The tyrant's people on both sides do fight,
    The noble Thanes do bravely in the war,
    The day almost itself professes yours,
    And little is to do.

MALCOLM
We have met with foes
That strike beside us.

SIWARD
Enter, sir, the castle.

Exeunt. Alarum.

SCENE VIII

Another part of the field.

Enter MACBETH.

MACBETH
Why should I play the Roman fool and die
On mine own sword? Whiles I see lives, the gashes
Do better upon them.

Enter MACDUFF.

MACDUFF
Turn, hell hound, turn!

MACBETH
Of all men else I have avoided thee.
But get thee back, my soul is too much charged
With blood of thine already.

MACDUFF
I have no words.
My voice is in my sword, thou bloodier villain
Than terms can give thee out!

They fight.

MACBETH
Thou losest labour.
As easy mayst thou the intrenchant air
With thy keen sword impress as make me bleed.
Let fall thy blade on vulnerable crests;
I bear a charmed life, which must not yield
To one of woman born.

MACDUFF
Despair thy charm,
And let the angel whom thou still hast served
Tell thee, Macduff was from his mother's womb
Untimely ripp'd.

MACBETH
Accursed be that tongue that tells me so,
For it hath cow'd my better part of man!
And be these juggling fiends no more believed
That patter with us in a double sense,
That keep the word of promise to our ear
And break it to our hope. I'll not fight with thee.

MACDUFF
Then yield thee, coward,
And live to be the show and gaze o' the time.
We'll have thee, as our rarer monsters are,
Painted upon a pole, and underwrit,
"Here may you see the tyrant."

MACBETH
I will not yield,
To kiss the ground before young Malcolm's feet,
And to be baited with the rabble's curse.
Though Birnam Wood be come to Dunsinane,
And thou opposed, being of no woman born,

Yet I will try the last. Before my body
I throw my warlike shield! Lay on, Macduff,
And damn'd be him that first cries, "Hold, enough!"

Exeunt fighting. Alarums.

SCENE IX

Another part of the battlefield.

Retreat. Flourish. Enter, with drum and colours,
MALCOLM, OLD SIWARD, ROSS, *the other* THANES,
and SOLDIERS.

MALCOLM
 I would the friends we miss were safe arrived.

SIWARD
 Some must go off, and yet, by these I see,
 So great a day as this is cheaply bought.

MALCOLM
 Macduff is missing, and your noble son.

ROSS
 Your son, my lord, has paid a soldier's debt.
 He only lived but till he was a man,
 The which no sooner had his prowess confirm'd
 In the unshrinking station where he fought,
 But like a man he died.

SIWARD
 Then he is dead?

ROSS

Ay, and brought off the field. Your cause of sorrow
Must not be measured by his worth, for then
It hath no end.

SIWARD

Had he his hurts before?

ROSS

Ay, on the front.

SIWARD

Why then, God's soldier be he!
Had I as many sons as I have hairs,
I would not wish them to a fairer death.
And so his knell is knoll'd.

MALCOLM

He's worth more sorrow,
And that I'll spend for him.

SIWARD

He's worth no more:
They say he parted well and paid his score,
And so God be with him! Here comes newer comfort.

Re-enter MACDUFF, *with* MACBETH'S *head.*

MACDUFF

Hail, King, for so thou art. Behold where stands
The usurper's cursed head. The time is free.
I see thee compass'd with thy kingdom's pearl
That speak my salutation in their minds,
Whose voices I desire aloud with mine –
Hail, King of Scotland!

ALL

Hail, King of Scotland! [*Flourish.*]

MALCOLM

    We shall not spend a large expense of time
    Before we reckon with your several loves
    And make us even with you. My Thanes and kinsmen,
    Henceforth be Earls, the first that ever Scotland
    In such an honour named. What's more to do,
    Which would be planted newly with the time,
    As calling home our exiled friends abroad
    That fled the snares of watchful tyranny,
    Producing forth the cruel ministers
    Of this dead butcher and his fiend-like queen,
    Who, as 'tis thought, by self and violent hands
    Took off her life; this, and what needful else
    That calls upon us, by the grace of Grace
    We will perform in measure, time, and place.
    So thanks to all at once and to each one,
    Whom we invite to see us crown'd at Scone.

Flourish. Exeunt.

Reading Questions

How should we feel about Lady Macbeth? What words would you use to describe her?

How does Shakespeare explore the idea that 'appearances can be deceptive' in Macbeth?

One of the witches says, 'something wicked this way comes'. What is the wicked thing?

Towards the end of the play, Macbeth says that he is no longer startled by frightening thoughts and sights. Explain what this shows about how he has changed during the play.

What does the play say about the typical expectations of a king in Macbeth's time?

GCSE 9-1 AQA ENGLISH MACBETH

AQA STUDY GUIDE

GCSE 9–1
MACBETH

BY WILLIAM SHAKESPEARE

REVISION &
PRACTICE
ALL IN ONE BOOK

Revision &
Practice Book

■SCHOLASTIC

GCSE 9-1 AQA Study Guides

The perfect preparation for the AQA English Literature closed book exams

Our new **GCSE 9-1 Study Guides** cover the AQA set texts in detail to really help you get to know your stuff. Including the full chronology of the text and focuses on key events, characters, themes, context, language and structure to help you demonstrate your knowledge and achieve higher marks.

With loads of practice questions (and answers) you can't go wrong!

Every study guide includes a free revision app
- Use the free, personalised digital revision planner
- Take quick tests to check your understanding
- Download free revision cards to help you revise on the go.
- Implement 'active' revision techniques to help the knowledge sink in

www.scholastic.co.uk/gcse

William Shakespeare was born in 1564, and grew up in the small town of Stratford-Upon-Avon in England before moving to London sometime around 1580. He wrote many plays, sonnets and poems, including such famous works as the tragedies *Hamlet* and *Macbeth*, the comedies *Much Ado About Nothing* and *A Midsummer's Night's Dream*, and the historical plays about English kings, such as Henry VI parts I and II. His plays are widely read and performed today, and his works are considered among the greatest works of literature in the English language. He died in 1616

Scholastic Classics

Louisa May Alcott:	*Little Women*
Jane Austen:	*Emma* *Pride and Prejudice* *Persuasion* *Sense and Sensibility*
L. Frank Baum:	*The Wonderful Wizard of Oz*
Anne Brontë:	*The Tenant of Wildfell Hall*
Charlotte Brontë:	*Jane Eyre*
Emily Brontë:	*Wuthering Heights*
Frances Hodgson Burnett: *The Secret Garden*	*A Little Princess*
Lewis Carroll:	*Alice's Adventures in Wonderland* *Alice Through the Looking Glass*
Susan Coolidge:	*What Katy Did*
Charles Dickens:	*A Christmas Carol* *Great Expectations* *Oliver Twist* *A Tale of Two Cities*

Arthur Conan Doyle:

The Adventures of Sherlock Holmes
The Sign of Four
The Hound of the Baskervilles

J. Meade Falkner:

Moonfleet

Kenneth Grahame:

The Wind in the Willows

Rudyard Kipling:

The Jungle Book

Jack London:

The Call of the Wild
White Fang

L. M. Montgomery:

Anne of Green Gables

E. Nesbit:

Five Children and It
The Railway Children

Edgar Allen Poe:

The Raven and Other Tales

Eleanor H Porter

Pollyanna

Anna Sewell:

Black Beauty

William Shakespeare:

Macbeth
Romeo and Juliet

Mary Shelley:

Frankenstein

Robert Louis Stevenson:

Kidnapped
Strange Case of Dr Jekyll Mr Hyde
Treasure Island